Infinity Prime Donna Casey

"This fractal is a classic spiral, which is my favorite, and I'm always amazed at the variations and the endlessly repeating patterns that can be created out of such a primary shape." – **Donna Casey**

Investigations
IN NUMBER, DATA, AND SPACE®

GRADE
K

How Many Do You Have?
Addition, Subtraction, and the Number System   UNIT 6

Editorial offices: Glenview, Illinois • Parsippany, New Jersey • New York, New York
Sales offices: Boston, Massachusetts • Duluth, Georgia
Glenview, Illinois • Coppell, Texas • Sacramento, California • Mesa, Arizona

scottforesman.com

The Investigations curriculum was developed by TERC, Cambridge, MA.

T E R C

This material is based on work supported by the National Science Foundation ("NSF") under Grant No. ESI-0095450. Any opinions, findings, and conclusions or recommendations expressed in this material are those of the author(s) and do not necessarily reflect the views of the National Science Foundation.

ISBN: 0-328-23725-6

ISBN: 978-0-328-23725-8

5 6 7 8 9 10-V003-15 14 13 12 11 10 09 08 07

CC:N1

Co-Principal Investigators

Susan Jo Russell

Karen Economopoulos

Authors

Lucy Wittenberg
Director Grades 3–5

Karen Economopoulos
Director Grades K–2

Virginia Bastable
(SummerMath for Teachers, Mt. Holyoke College)

Katie Hickey Bloomfield

Keith Cochran

Darrell Earnest

Arusha Hollister

Nancy Horowitz

Erin Leidl

Megan Murray

Young Oh

Beth W. Perry

Susan Jo Russell

Deborah Schifter
(Education Development Center)

Kathy Sillman

Administrative Staff

Amy Taber
Project Manager

Beth Bergeron

Lorraine Brooks

Emi Fujiwara

Contributing Authors

Denise Baumann

Jennifer DiBrienza

Hollee Freeman

Paula Hooper

Jan Mokros

Stephen Monk
(University of Washington)

Mary Beth O'Connor

Judy Storeygard

Cornelia Tierney

Elizabeth Van Cleef

Carol Wright

Technology

Jim Hammerman

Classroom Field Work

Amy Appell

Rachel E. Davis

Traci Higgins

Julia Thompson

Collaborating Teachers

This group of dedicated teachers carried out extensive field testing in their classrooms, met regularly to discuss issues of teaching and learning mathematics, provided feedback to staff, welcomed staff into their classrooms to document students' work, and contributed both suggestions and written material that has been incorporated into the curriculum.

Bethany Altchek

Linda Amaral

Kimberly Beauregard

Barbara Bernard

Nancy Buell

Rose Christiansen

Chris Colbath-Hess

Lisette Colon

Kim Cook

Frances Cooper

Kathleen Drew

Rebeka Eston Salemi

Thomas Fisher

Michael Flynn

Holly Ghazey

Susan Gillis

Danielle Harrington

Elaine Herzog

Francine Hiller

Kirsten Lee Howard

Liliana Klass

Leslie Kramer

Melissa Lee Andrichak

Kelley Lee Sadowski

Jennifer Levitan

Mary Lou LoVecchio

Kristen McEnaney

Maura McGrail

Kathe Millett

Florence Molyneaux

Amy Monkiewicz

Elizabeth Monopoli

Carol Murray

Robyn Musser

Christine Norrman

Deborah O'Brien

Timothy O'Connor

Anne Marie O'Reilly

Mark Paige

Margaret Riddle

Karen Schweitzer

Elisabeth Seyferth

Susan Smith

Debra Sorvillo

Shoshanah Starr

Janice Szymaszek

Karen Tobin

JoAnn Trauschke

Ana Vaisenstein

Yvonne Watson

Michelle Woods

Mary Wright

Note: Unless otherwise noted, all contributors listed above were staff of the Education Research Collaborative at TERC during their work on the curriculum. Other affiliations during the time of development are listed.

Advisors

Deborah Lowenberg Ball,
University of Michigan

Hyman Bass, Professor of Mathematics and Mathematics Education
University of Michigan

Mary Canner, Principal, Natick Public Schools

Thomas Carpenter, Professor of Curriculum and Instruction,
University of Wisconsin-Madison

Janis Freckmann, Elementary Mathematics Coordinator,
Milwaukee Public Schools

Lynne Godfrey, Mathematics Coach,
Cambridge Public Schools

Ginger Hanlon, Instructional Specialist in Mathematics,
New York City Public Schools

DeAnn Huinker, Director, Center for Mathematics and
Science Education Research, University of Wisconsin-Milwaukee

James Kaput, Professor of Mathematics, University of
Massachusetts-Dartmouth

Kate Kline, Associate Professor, Department of Mathematics
and Statistics, Western Michigan University

Jim Lewis, Professor of Mathematics,
University of Nebraska-Lincoln

William McCallum, Professior of Mathematics,
University of Arizona

Harriet Pollatsek, Professor of Mathematics,
Mount Holyoke College

Debra Shein-Gerson, Elementary Mathematics Specialist,
Weston Public Schools

Gary Shevell, Assistant Principal,
New York City Public Schools

Liz Sweeney, Elementary Math Department,
Boston Public Schools

Lucy West, Consultant, Metamorphosis:
Teaching Learning Communities, Inc.

This revision of the curriculum was built on the work of the many authors who contributed to the first edition (published between 1994 and 1998). We acknowledge the critical contributions of these authors in developing the content and pedagogy of *Investigations*:

Authors

Joan Akers

Michael T. Battista

Douglas H. Clements

Karen Economopoulos

Marlene Kliman

Jan Mokros

Megan Murray

Ricardo Nemirovsky

Andee Rubin

Susan Jo Russell

Cornelia Tierney

Contributing Authors

Mary Berle-Carman

Rebecca B. Corwin

Rebeka Eston

Claryce Evans

Anne Goodrow

Cliff Konold

Chris Mainhart

Sue McMillen

Jerrie Moffet

Tracy Noble

Kim O'Neil

Mark Ogonowski

Julie Sarama

Amy Shulman Weinberg

Margie Singer

Virginia Woolley

Tracey Wright

Contents

UNIT 6

How Many Do You Have?

Investigations

CURRICULUM

Overview of Program Components

The **Curriculum Units** are the teaching guides. (See far right.)

Implementing Investigations in Kindergarten offers suggestions for implementing the curriculum. It also contains a comprehensive index.

The **Resources Binder** contains all the Resource Masters that support instruction. (Also available on CD) The binder also includes a student software CD.

FOR STUDENTS

The **Student Activity Book** contains the consumable student pages (Recording Sheets, Homework, Practice, and so on).

The **Student Math Handbook Flip Chart** contains pictures of Math Words and Ideas pages.

The *Investigations* Curriculum

Investigations in Number, Data, and Space® is a K–5 mathematics curriculum designed to engage students in making sense of mathematical ideas. Six major goals guided the development of the *Investigations in Number, Data, and Space®* curriculum. The curriculum is designed to:

- Support students to make sense of mathematics and learn that they can be mathematical thinkers

- Focus on computational fluency with whole numbers as a major goal of the elementary grades

- Provide substantive work in important areas of mathematics—rational numbers, geometry, measurement, data, and early algebra—and connections among them

- Emphasize reasoning about mathematical ideas

- Communicate mathematics content and pedagogy to teachers

- Engage the range of learners in understanding mathematics

Underlying these goals are three guiding principles that are touchstones for the *Investigations* team as we approach both students and teachers as agents of their own learning:

1. *Students have mathematical ideas.* Students come to school with ideas about numbers, shapes, measurements, patterns, and data. If given the opportunity to learn in an environment that stresses making sense of mathematics, students build on the ideas they already have and learn about new mathematics they have never encountered. Students learn that they are capable of having mathematical ideas, applying what they know to new situations, and thinking and reasoning about unfamiliar problems.

2. *Teachers are engaged in ongoing learning* about mathematics content, pedagogy, and student learning. The curriculum provides material for professional development, to be used by teachers individually or in groups, that supports teachers' continued learning as they use the curriculum over several years. The *Investigations* curriculum materials are designed as much to be a dialogue with teachers as to be a core of content for students.

3. *Teachers collaborate with the students and curriculum materials* to create the curriculum as enacted in the classroom. The only way for a good curriculum to be used well is for teachers to be active participants in implementing it. Teachers use the curriculum to maintain a clear, focused, and coherent agenda for mathematics teaching. At the same time, they observe and listen carefully to students, try to understand how they are thinking, and make teaching decisions based on these observations.

Investigations is based on experience from research and practice, including field testing that involved documentation of thousands of hours in classrooms, observations of students, input from teachers, and analysis of student work. As a result, the curriculum addresses the learning needs of real students in a wide range of classrooms and communities. The investigations are carefully designed to invite all students into mathematics—girls and boys; members of diverse cultural, ethnic, and language groups; and students with a wide variety of strengths, needs, and interests.

Based on this extensive classroom testing, the curriculum takes seriously the time students need to develop a strong conceptual foundation and skills based on that foundation. Each curriculum unit focuses on an area of content in depth, providing time for students to develop and practice ideas across a variety of activities and contexts that build on each other. Daily guidelines for time spent on class sessions, Classroom Routines (K–3), and Ten-Minute Math (3–5) reflect the commitment to devoting adequate time to mathematics in each school day.

About This Curriculum Unit

This **Curriculum Unit** is one of seven teaching guides in Grade K. The sixth unit in Grade K is *How Many Do You Have?*

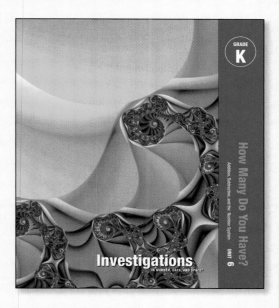

- The **Introduction and Overview** section organizes and presents the instructional materials, provides background information, and highlights important features specific to this unit.

- Each Curriculum Unit contains several **Investigations.** Each Investigation focuses on a set of related mathematical ideas.

- Investigations are divided into 30–45 minute **Sessions,** or lessons.

- Sessions have a combination of these parts: **Activity, Discussion, Math Workshop,** and **Session Follow-Up.**

- Each session also has one or more **Classroom Routines** that are done outside of math time.

- At the back of the book is a collection of **Teacher Notes** and **Dialogue Boxes** that provide professional development related to the unit.

- Also included at the back of the book are the **Student Math Handbook Flip Chart** pages for this unit.

- The **Index** provides a way to look up important words or terms.

Overview

O F   T H I S   U N I T

Investigation	Session	Day	
INVESTIGATION 1 **Numbers of Tiles** Students investigate combinations of numbers as they arrange tiles and explore different ways a set of two-color counters can land. They consider how notation can represent such situations.	**1.1** Six Tiles in All	1	
	1.2 Toss the Chips	2	
	1.3 Arrangements of Five Through Ten Tiles	3	
	1.4 Counting Jar	4	
	1.5 Racing Bears	5	
	1.6 Arranging Five Tiles	6	
	1.7 Arranging Eight Tiles	7	
INVESTIGATION 2 **Counting and Measuring** Students count and represent quantities to 20. They revisit ideas in measurement as they find out how long different parts of their bodies are.	**2.1** Collect 15 Together	8	
	2.2 Inventory Bags	9	
	2.3 Measuring Ourselves	10	
	2.4 Do We Have to Count Them All?	11	
	2.5 How Did You Count?	12	
	2.6 Representing an Inventory	13	

Each *Investigations* session has some combination of these four parts: **Activity, Discussion, Math Workshop,** and **Session Follow-Up.** These session parts are indicated in the chart below. Each session also has one or more **Classroom Routines** that are done outside of math time.

Activity	Discussion	Math Workshop	Assessment Checklist*	Session Follow-Up
● ● ●	●			●
●	●	●		●
●	●	●	●	●
	●	●	●	●
● ●	●			●
●	●	●		●
●	●	●		●
●	●	●		●
●	●	●		●
●	●	●		●
	● ●	●		●
	● ●	●		●
●	●	●	●	●

Classroom Routines

Calendar	Attendance	Today's Question	Patterns on the Pocket Chart
	●		
		●	
●			
	●		
			●
		●	
●			
			●
	●		
		●	
●			
			●
	●		

*An Assessment Checklist is introduced in this session.

Overview

O F   T H I S   U N I T

Investigation	Session	Day	
INVESTIGATION 3 **How Many in All?** Students count and compare quantities to 20. The class revisits addition and subtraction situations, including story problems, which students now model, solve, and represent on paper.	**3.1** Roll and Record 3	14	
	3.2 Double Compare	15	
	3.3 Modeling Story Problems	16	
	3.4 Build and Remove	17	
	3.5 How Many Balls?	18	
	3.6 How Do You Show the One That Is Gone?	19	
	3.7 How Many Blocks?	20	
INVESTIGATION 4 **How Many of Each?** Students further investigate combinations of numbers through a story problem context, "How Many of Each?", and other activities.	**4.1** Five Crayons in All	21	
	4.2 Combinations of Six	22	
	4.3 Total of Six	23	
	4.4 Six Crayons in All	24	
	4.5 More Combinations of Six and End-of-Unit Assessment	25	
	4.6 End-of-Unit Assessment and Combinations of Six	26	

Activity	Discussion	Math Workshop	Assessment Checklist*	Session Follow-Up
●●		●		●
●	●	●		●
●	●	●		●
●●		●		●
●	●	●		●
●	●	●		●
●	●	●		●
●●	●			●
	●	●		●
●	●	●		●
●	●	●		●
	●●	●		●
	●	●		●

Classroom Routines

Calendar	Attendance	Today's Question	Patterns on the Pocket Chart
		●	
			●
●			
	●		
		●	
●			
			●
	●		
		●	
●			
			●
	●		
		●	

*An Assessment Checklist is introduced in this session.

Mathematics

IN THIS UNIT

How Many Do You Have? is the sixth of seven units in the Kindergarten sequence, and the third of three units in the Kindergarten number strand. These units develop ideas about counting and quantity, comparison, linear measurement, the composition of numbers, and the operations of addition and subtraction. The mathematical focus of *this* unit is on counting sets of up to 20 objects; decomposing the numbers to 10 in a variety of different ways (e.g., 7 can be seen as 5 and 2 or as 3 and 2 and 2); using numbers, and notation where appropriate, to describe arrangements of tiles and other addition situations; and finding and exploring combinations of a number. Students continue to develop an understanding of the operations of addition and subtraction as they act out, model, and solve story problems, and play games that involve combining or separating small amounts.

 LOOKING BACK This unit builds on the work in *Counting and Comparing* and *Measuring and Counting*, which gave students many opportunities to develop their sense of numbers and quantities to 10, to count and compare amounts to 15, and to measure objects through direct comparison and the use of multiple nonstandard units (e.g., a set of craft sticks). Students began making sense of the operations of addition and subtraction by acting out stories and playing games that involved combining or separating small amounts. For example, students were asked to find the total after a small amount was added (or taken away), and to figure out what needed to be added (or taken away) to make a set of a given size.

This unit focuses on 4 Mathematical Emphases:

1 Counting and Quantity Developing strategies for accurately counting a set of objects by ones

Math Focus Points

- Developing and analyzing visual images for quantities up to 10

- Developing strategies for accurately counting and keeping track of quantities up to 20

- Using subsets to count a set of objects

- Counting spaces and moving on a gameboard

In this unit, students get repeated practice with counting and developing visual images for quantities to ten as they try to remember and rebuild images made with square tiles and as they find different ways to arrange sets of five to ten tiles.

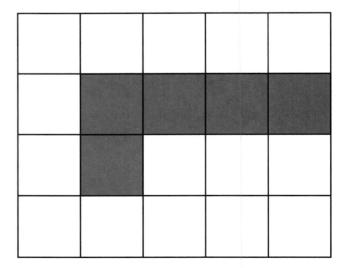

Students also count larger amounts in a variety of contexts. For example, they play *Collect 20 Together,* take inventory of bags containing up to 20 related objects, investigate a Counting Jar with 20 objects in it, and use cubes to measure parts of their bodies. The larger totals require that students learn a new sequence of number names and numerals and that they refine their strategies for organizing and keeping track of the objects they are counting. As in *Measuring and Counting,* many of the counting activities work to build a bridge, connecting counting to the operation of addition, by asking students to add a small amount to a set and figure out, "How many now?" This encourages students to begin combining small amounts rather than counting whole collections from one each time.

2 Whole Number Operations **Making sense of and developing strategies to solve addition and subtraction problems with small numbers**

Math Focus Points

- ◈ Decomposing numbers in different ways

- ◈ Finding the total after 1, 2, or 3 is added to, or subtracted from, a set

- ◈ Combining two single-digit numbers, with totals to 20

- ◈ Modeling the action of combining and separating situations

- ◈ Separating one amount from another

- ◈ Developing strategies for solving addition and subtraction story problems

- ◈ Finding combinations of five and six

- ◈ Considering combinations of a number (e.g., 6 is 3 and 3 and also 5 and 1)

In this unit, students work with combinations of quantities that they can count fluently. As they find ways to arrange and describe sets of five through ten square tiles or record combinations of two-color counters, they begin to see that numbers can be composed in different ways. Throughout this unit, students work on activities that involve seeing and describing a given quantity (e.g. five tiles) as made up of groups (e.g. a group of three and a group of two).

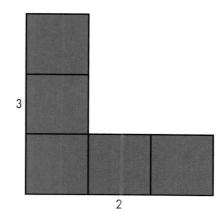

They are also asked to decompose quantities (e.g. five can be split into three and two) and to find one or more combinations of a quantity (e.g. five can be five and zero, two and three or four and one.) All of this work lays the foundation for making meaningful sense of $3 + 2 = 5$, or even $5 - 3 = 2$, in later years.

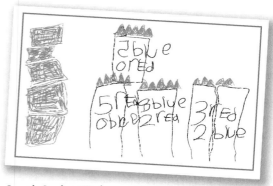

Sample Student Work

Sample Student Work

Students continue to develop an understanding of the operations of addition and subtraction as they retell, act out, model and solve story problems about combining and separating. The focus remains on making sense of the action of a problem. This ability to visualize the actions of combining or joining and removing or separating form the basis for students' problem solving throughout the grades. Students also play a variety of games that model the operations of addition and subtraction. Although kindergarteners may use counting strategies as they play these games, they are having repeated experiences with joining two or more amounts, and with removing an amount from a whole. Young students develop their understanding of the operations of addition and subtraction by having many opportunities to count, visualize, model, solve, and discuss different types of problems.

3 Whole Number Operations Using manipulatives, drawings, tools, and notation to show strategies and solutions

Math Focus Points

◆ Using numbers, and/or addition notation, to describe arrangements of objects, to record how many, and to represent an addition situation

◆ Using numbers, pictures, and/or words to represent a quantity, measurement, or a solution to a problem

Throughout the *Investigations* curriculum, students use mathematical tools and representations to model and solve problems and to clarify and communicate their thinking. In this unit, students use tiles and Ten-Frames to represent quantities to 10; cubes to model addition and subtraction story problems; and numbers, words, or drawings to represent inventories, body measurements, and solutions to problems about combining, separating, and combinations.

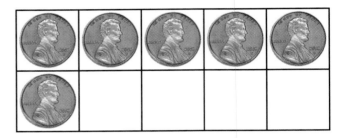

In this unit there is an explicit focus on using written numbers to describe arrangements and to represent quantities and number words (e.g., when students see * * * or hear "three," they can write "3"). In addition, the use of addition notation is modeled where it matches the thinking of a student. When students are asked to represent mathematical work on paper, they are encouraged to do so in ways that make sense to them. Students learn how to communicate mathematical information by having many opportunities to record, and to see and interpret the ways others—including their teacher and classmates—record.

This Unit also focuses on

◆ Creating an equivalent set

◆ Thinking strategically about moves on a gameboard

◆ Repeating multiple nonstandard units to quantify length

◆ Counting and comparing quantities to 20 to determine which is more

◆ Beginning to recognize that some problems have more than one solution

Classroom Routines focus on

◆ Developing strategies for counting accurately

◆ Considering whether order matters when you count

◆ Comparing quantities

◆ Counting forward and backward

◆ Using the calendar as a tool for keeping track of time

◆ Collecting, counting, representing, describing, and comparing data

◆ Determining what comes next in a repeating pattern

◆ Describing repeating patterns

LOOKING FORWARD

The work in this unit is built upon as students turn to the data unit, which involves counting and solving problems about the number of students in the class. It also lays the foundation for the number work in first grade, which continues to focus on ideas about counting and quantity, the composition of numbers, and the operations of addition and subtraction.

Assessment

IN THIS UNIT

Most sessions in this unit provide an opportunity for Ongoing Assessment. In addition, assessment checklists are provided to keep track of your observations about students' work with concepts and ideas that are benchmarks for this unit.

ONGOING ASSESSMENT: Observing Students at Work

The following sessions provide **Ongoing Assessment: Observing Students at Work** opportunities:

- **Session 1.1, p. 32**
- **Session 1.2, p. 37**
- **Session 1.3, p. 43**
- **Session 1.4, p. 48**
- **Session 1.5, p. 53**
- **Session 2.1, p. 70**

- **Session 2.2, p. 76**
- **Session 2.3, p. 81**
- **Session 2.4, p. 85**
- **Session 2.6, p. 92**
- **Session 3.1, p. 102**
- **Session 3.2, p. 107**

- **Session 3.4, p. 117**
- **Session 3.5, p. 121**
- **Session 3.6, p. 125**
- **Session 3.7, p. 130**
- **Session 4.1, p. 139**
- **Session 4.3, p. 149**

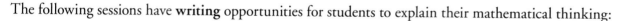

WRITING OPPORTUNITIES

The following sessions have **writing** opportunities for students to explain their mathematical thinking:

- **Session 2.2, pp. 75–76**
  Student Activity Book, p. 56

- **Session 3.5, p. 120**
  Student Activity Book, p. 63

- **Session 3.6, p. 124**
  Student Activity Book, p. 64

- **Session 4.1, pp. 139–140**
  Student Activity Book, p. 66

- **Session 4.4, p. 152**
  Student Activity Book, p. 68

PORTFOLIO OPPORTUNITIES

The following sessions have work appropriate for a **portfolio:**

- **Session 1.3, p. 43**
  Arrangements of Five Through Ten Tiles

- **Session 1.4, p. 47**
  Counting Jar

- **Sessions 2.2, p. 75**
  Student Activity Book, p. 56

- **Session 2.6, p. 92**
  Counting Jar

- **Session 3.1, p. 101**
  Student Activity Book, p. 59

- **Session 3.6, p. 124**
  Student Activity Book, p. 64

- **Session 3.7, p. 129**
  Student Activity Book, p. 65

- **Session 4.1, pp. 139–140**
  Student Activity Book, p. 66

- **Session 4.4, p. 152**
  Student Activity Book, p. 68

Assessing the Benchmarks

Observing students as they engage in conversation about their ideas is a primary means to assess their mathematical understanding. Consider all of your students' work, not just the written assessments. See the chart below for suggestions about key activities to observe.

Assessment Checklists are introduced in Session 1.3, Session 1.4, and Session 2.6. Consult these charts to determine which students need to complete an End-of-Unit Assessment interview. Over the course of Sessions 4.5 and 4.6, you will meet individually with students who have not yet clearly met each benchmark or who you have questions about.

 Checklist Available

Benchmarks in This Unit	Key Activities to Observe	Assessment
1. Write the numbers to 10.	**Sessions 1.3–1.4, 1.6–1.7:** Arrangements of Five Through Ten Tiles **Sessions 1.2–1.4, 4.2–4.6:** *Toss the Chips* **Sessions 3.1–3.7:** *Roll and Record 3*	**Session 1.3 Assessment Checklist:** Writing Numbers to 10 ✓ **Session 1.4 Assessment Checklist:** Counting ✓
2. Count a set of up to 20 objects.	**Sessions 1.4, 1.6–1.7, 2.1:** Counting Jar **Sessions 2.2–2.6:** Inventory Bags **Sessions 2.2–2.6:** *Collect 20 Together* **Session 2.3–2.6:** Measuring Ourselves	**Session 2.6 Assessment Checklist:** Addition ✓
3. Combine two small quantities.	**Sessions 2.6, 3.1–3.3:** Counting Jar **Sessions 3.1–3.7:** *Roll and Record 3* **Sessions 3.1, 3.3–3.7:** Story Problems **Sessions 3.2–3.7:** *Double Compare*	

Relating the Mathematical Emphases to the Benchmarks

Mathematical Emphases	Benchmarks
Whole Number Operations Using manipulatives, drawings, tools, and notation to show strategies and solutions	1
Counting and Quantity Developing strategies for accurately counting a set of objects by ones	2
Whole Number Operations Making sense of and developing strategies to solve addition and subtraction problems with small numbers	3

Algebra Connections

This unit provides opportunities for students to engage with ideas that lay a foundation for algebra. Five- and six-year-olds can and do think algebraically. Part of the work of Kindergarten is helping students learn to verbalize those thoughts, both as a way to engage with generalizations about numbers and operations and as a foundation for meaningful use of algebraic notation in the future.

Throughout Kindergarten, students have many opportunities to work with contexts that involve combining and decomposing quantities: six tiles can be arranged as a row of four and a row of two; when 6 two-color counters are tossed, they may land showing four red and two yellow; when two counters are added to a pile of four counters, the resulting pile contains six counters. As students come to recognize that these numerical relationships remain constant across different contexts, they develop an understanding of the operation of addition. That is, what had once been very different actions—arranging a set of tiles, tossing a set of chips, and collecting counters—are now subsumed under one operation.

Furthermore, through their engagement with various additive contexts, students begin to generalize how the operation behaves. For example, consider the following discussion of a story problem:

Yoshio was in charge of cleaning up after recess. He found three balls by the swings. Then he found two more by the slide.

Before the teacher poses the problem the students are to solve, she asks them to retell the story.

Hugo: There were balls by the swing and the slide.

Carmen: There was three and two.

Raul: At first there were three balls and then two more.

Then, before asking students to find the total number of balls, the teacher asks them what they expect:

Teacher: Yoshio found three balls by the swing and two more by the slide. Do you think Yoshio had more than three balls or fewer than three balls at the end of the story?

Tammy: At first he found three and then two more.

Manuel: So more than three.

Kaitlyn: Yeah, he found three and then some *more*.

The question the teacher asks—Did Yoshio find more than three or fewer than three?—draws students' attention to an important feature of the addition of counting numbers: when quantities are added, the result is greater than either of the addends.

This is in contrast to some other contexts students encounter; for example, when they are given the following problem:

Mia brought grapes for snack. She had five grapes. Then she ate one of the grapes. How many grapes did Mia have left?

Before finding the number of grapes Mia had left, the teacher asks, "Does Mia have more than or fewer than five grapes at the end of the story?" In this problem, which involves separating or removing—a context students will later associate with subtraction—the result is less.

Thus, the generalization these Kindergarten students are approaching might be stated as: when adding (with the number they know), the resulting amount is greater than you started with. When subtracting (with the numbers they know), the resulting amount is less than you started with.

However, as students learn about new kinds of numbers, many of their generalizations, like this one, will have to be rethought. As students encounter zero, they will have to consider how the operations behave with this new number. Their generalizations will become, "When adding, the resulting amount is greater than you started with, except when you add zero, and then the result is the same number you started with." And, "when subtracting, the resulting amount is less than you started with, except when you subtract zero, and then the result is the same number you started with."

Still later, students will encounter negative numbers, and will need to revise these generalizations again. After all, $4 + (-1) = 3$. In this case, the result, 3, is smaller than the starting amount, 4. Therefore, the statement will need to be further refined: "When adding a positive number, the resulting amount is greater than you started with; when adding zero, the result is the same as you started with; and when adding a negative number, the resulting amount is less than you started with."

Even if generalizations will need to be refined as the number domain expands, it is important for students to have opportunities to consider and verbalize their observations about how the operations behave. When restricted to the domain of counting numbers (1, 2, 3, 4, . . .), the numbers these kindergarteners know, the original statement is true. It is on the basis of such

generalizations that students develop number sense, learn to estimate, and make sense of calculation procedures. And it is on the basis of such understandings that students will make sense of algebraic notation years from now. When that time comes, as students represent the ideas discussed in this essay, it will be critical that they specify values for which generalizations are true: for any number x and for any positive number y, $x + y > x$ and $x - y < x$.

Note: In the text for the sessions, you will find flags that identify where these early algebra discussions are likely to occur. Some of the **Teacher Notes** and **Dialogue Boxes** further elaborate the ideas and illustrate students' conversations about them.

Classroom Routines

Classroom Routines offer practice and review of key concepts for this grade level. These daily activities, to be done in 10 minutes outside of math class, occur in a regular rotation every 4–5 days. Specific directions for the day's routine are provided in each session. For the full description and variations of each classroom routine, see *Implementing Investigations in Kindergarten*.

Attendance

Students continue to count to determine the total number of students present and to explore what happens when the count begins with different students. In order to help students connect the counting numbers to the quantities they represent, the class discusses how many students have counted midway through the count. Students also compare two groups, determine which group has more, and determine how many more there are in this larger group. They also practice the counting sequence in reverse and begin to see the connection between counting forward and backward.

Math Focus Points

- Developing strategies for counting accurately
- Considering whether order matters when you count
- Comparing quantities
- Counting forward and backward

Calendar

Students continue to review the numbers and counting sequence to 31 as well as the names and sequence of the days of the week. Students also use the calendar to determine how many days until (or since) a special event and explain their strategies.

Math Focus Points

- Using the calendar as a tool for keeping track of time
- Developing strategies for counting accurately

Today's Question

Students record their response to a survey question with two possible answers on a two-column table. Class discussion focuses on describing and interpreting the data.

Math Focus Points

- Collecting, counting, representing, describing, and comparing data

Patterns on the Pocket Chart

Students see part of a repeating pattern. They describe and extend the pattern and determine what would come next if the pattern were to continue. In this unit students also consider patterns that take up more than one row in the pocket chart, and they determine what comes farther down the line in a repeating pattern, rather than what comes next.

Math Focus Points

- Determining what comes next in a repeating pattern
- Describing repeating patterns

Practice and Review

IN THIS UNIT

Practice and review play a critical role in the *Investigations* program. The following components and features are available to provide regular reinforcement of key mathematical concepts and procedures.

Books	Features	In This Unit ...
Curriculum Unit	**Classroom Routines** offer practice and review of key concepts for this grade level. These daily activities, to be done in ten minutes outside of math class, occur in a regular rotation every 4–5 days. Specific directions for the day's routine are provided in each session. For the full description and variations of each classroom routine see *Implementing Investigations in Kindergarten*.	• **All sessions**
Student Activity Book	**Practice** pages in the *Student Activity Book* provide one of two types of written practice: **reinforcement** of the content of the unit or **enrichment** opportunities.	• **Session 1.6** • **Session 2.6** • **Session 3.1** • **Session 3.3** • **Session 4.1** • **Session 4.3** • **Session 4.5**
	Homework pages in the *Student Activity Book* are an extension of the work done in class. At times they help students prepare for upcoming activities.	• **No homework in this unit**
Student Math Handbook Flip Chart	**Math Words and Ideas** in the *Student Math Handbook Flip Chart* are pages that summarize key words and ideas. Most Words and Ideas pages have at least one exercise.	• **Student Math Handbook Flip Chart, pp. 11–13, 19–21, 26–34, 38**

Supporting the Range of Learners

Sessions	1.1	1.2	1.3	1.5	1.6	1.7	2.1	2.2	2.3	3.1	3.2	3.3	3.4	3.5	3.6	3.7	4.1	4.2	4.3	4.4
Intervention	•		•	•			•	•	•	•	•	•		•	•	•	•		•	•
Extension		•	•		•	•		•	•	•							•	•		•
ELL		•					•					•					•			

Intervention

Suggestions are made to support and engage students who are having difficulty.

Extension

Suggestions are made to support and engage students who finish early or may be ready for additional challenge.

English Language Learners (ELL)

In this unit, students count sets of up to 20 objects and decompose numbers to 10 in a variety of ways. They must therefore become fluent in the rote counting sequence of the numbers 1–20. Since English Language Learners may be unfamiliar with the number names in English, they will need additional opportunities to practice these numbers in context.

Students must also understand addition- and subtraction-related words such as *plus, combine, put together, join, add, minus, take away,* and *equals.* Model the relevant language in context and encourage students to use these terms themselves.

English Language Learners may need additional vocabulary support to help them visualize the action of story problems. Use pictures, objects, actions, and gestures to illustrate unfamiliar vocabulary. Read problems out loud and have volunteers act them out. When English Language Learners act out these problems, support their language growth by putting words to their actions. Kiyo, I see you made a group of five counters to *represent* Mia's grapes. Then you took one away to *represent* the grape that Mia ate. How many counters do you have now? How many grapes does Mia have left?

Working with the Range of Learners: Classroom Cases is a set of episodes written by teachers that focuses on meeting the needs of the range of learners in the classroom. In the first section, *Setting up the Mathematical Community,* teachers write about how they create a supportive and productive learning environment in their classrooms. In the next section, *Accommodations for Learning,* teachers focus on specific modifications they make to meet the needs of some of their learners. In the last section, *Language and Representation,* teachers share how they help students use representations and develop language to investigate and express mathematical ideas. The questions at the end of each case provide a starting point for your own reflection or for discussion with colleagues. See *Implementing Investigations in Kindergarten* for this set of episodes.

Mathematical Emphases

Counting and Quantity Developing strategies for accurately counting a set of objects by 1s

Math Focus Points

◆ Developing and analyzing visual images for quantities up to 10

◆ Developing strategies for accurately counting and keeping track of quantities up to 20

◆ Creating an equivalent set

◆ Counting spaces and moving on a gameboard

Whole Number Operations Making sense of and developing strategies to solve addition and subtraction problems with small numbers

Math Focus Points

◆ Decomposing numbers in different ways

Whole Number Operations Using manipulatives, drawings, tools, and notation to show strategies and solutions

Math Focus Points

◆ Using numbers, and/or addition notation, to describe arrangements of objects and to record how many

This Investigation also focuses on

◆ Thinking strategically about moves on a gameboard

Number of Tiles

	Student Activity Book	Student Math Handbook Flip Chart	Professional Development: Read Ahead of Time	
SESSION 1.1 p. 28				
Six Tiles in All Students revisit *Quick Images* with a focus on using numbers and addition notation to describe arrangements of square tiles. Then, they find different ways to arrange six square tiles so that each tile shares a whole side with the tile next to it, and record at least one arrangement.		27, 28, 29	• **Mathematics in This Unit,** p. 12 • **Teacher Note:** Introducing Notation in Kindergarten, p. 163 • **Dialogue Box:** Pictures and Numbers, p. 184	
SESSION 1.2 p. 35				
Toss the Chips Students revisit *Toss the Chips*, a game in which students drop a set of two-color counters and record the number of red and the number of yellow. Math Workshop and class discussion focuses on different ways to decompose a set of six into parts.	53			
SESSION 1.3 p. 41				
Arrangements of Five Through Ten Tiles Students make and record arrangements of square tiles for the numbers five through ten. Math Workshop focuses on combinations of numbers. Class discussion focuses on ways to use numbers, and addition notation where appropriate, to describe an arrangement of tiles.		27, 28		

Classroom Routines See page 20 for an overview.

Attendance
- **No materials needed**

Today's Question
- *Today's Question* charts for Session 1.2 and 1.6. See instructions on pages 35 and 55.

Calendar
- **Class calendar or pocket calendar**

Patterns on a Pocket Chart
- **Pocket Chart(s)**
- **M7, Question Mark Cards** Cut apart.
- **Prepared cups or bags of pattern blocks (1 per pair)**

Materials to Gather	Materials to Prepare
• **Chart paper** • **Square tiles** Sort by color. (1 bin) • **Small paper cups with 10 tiles** (1 per student; optional) • **Envelope or folder for storing work with tiles** (1 per student; optional) • **Colored paper** • **Glue** • **Coloring materials** (that match the colors of the square tiles)	• **M1, Inch Grid Paper** Make copies. (12 per student; plus extras) • **Chart paper** Draw several images that use 6 squares each on a piece of chart paper. See pages 29–30. • **Paper squares** Cut colored paper that matches the color of the square tiles into one-inch squares. (Use paper students can write on in pencil.) Distribute the squares, separated by color, to different workstations in resealable plastic bags. (approximately 100 per student)
• **Two-color counters** • **Chart paper** • **Square tiles** • **Materials for Six Tiles in All** See Session 1.1.	• **M2, *Toss the Chips*** Make copies. (as needed) • **M3–M4, Family Letter** Make copies. (1 per student)
• **Chart paper** • **Square tiles** • **Materials for *Toss the Chips*** See Session 1.2. • **Materials for Six Tiles in All, for use in Arrangements of Five through Ten Tiles** See Session 1.1.	• **M5, Assessment Checklist: Writing Numbers to 10** ☑ Make copies. (3–4 per class; plus extras as needed)

☑ Checklist Available

Number of Tiles, *continued*

	Student Activity Book	Student Math Handbook Flip Chart	Professional Development: Read Ahead of Time	
SESSION 1.4 p. 46				
Counting Jar Class begins with a discussion focused on ways to use numbers, and addition notation where appropriate, to describe an arrangement of tiles. Math Workshop follows, which includes the Counting Jar with 20 objects placed in it.		20, 27, 28		
SESSION 1.5 p. 50				
Racing Bears Students play a new version of *Racing Bears*, a game that involves counting and decomposing numbers. Class discussion focuses on strategies for splitting rolls to collect counters.	54	27, 28		
SESSION 1.6 p. 55				
Arranging Five Tiles Students are introduced to the class book of *Ways to Make Numbers*. Math Workshop continues. Class ends with students looking at the different ways the class discovered to arrange five tiles.	55	28–29		
SESSION 1.7 p. 59				
Arranging Eight Tiles Math Workshop continues, and class discussion focuses on the different ways the class discovered to arrange eight tiles.		27, 28		

Materials to Gather	Materials to Prepare
• **Materials for the Counting Jar routine** (as you have set it up) • **Student's recorded tile arrangements** (from previous sessions) • **Materials for Arrangements of Five Through Ten Tiles** See Session 1.3. • **Materials for *Toss the Chips*** See Session 1.2. • **Chart paper**	• **M6, Assessment Checklist: Counting** ☑ (3–4 per class, plus extras as needed) • **Counting Jar** Place 20 objects in the jar.
• **Teddy bear or other counters** (1 bin per pair) • **1-to-6 dot cubes** (1 per pair) • **Other small counters such as buttons, beads, or pennies** (4 per pair)	• **M8, *Racing Bears* Gameboard** Make copies. (1 per pair, ideally on card stock and/or laminated) You may have made these in the unit *Measuring and Counting*.
• **1-to-3 dot cubes** (optional) • **Materials for *Racing Bears*** See Session 1.5. • **Materials for Counting Jar** See Session 1.4. • **Materials for Arrangements of Five Through Ten Tiles** See Session 1.3. • **Connecting cubes** (optional)	• ***Ways to Make Numbers* Class Book** Prepare 3 pages of the book that show the different ways students found to arrange 5, 6, and 7 square tiles. See the Teaching Notes on pages 48 and 54.
• **Materials for *Racing Bears*** See Session 1.5. • **Materials for Counting Jar** See Session 1.4. • **Materials for Arrangements of Five Through Ten Tiles** See Session 1.3.	• ***Ways to Make Numbers* Class Book** Prepare 3 pages of the book that show the different ways students found to arrange 8, 9, and 10 square tiles. See the Teaching Notes on pages 48 and 58.

☑ Checklist Available

Six Tiles in All

Math Focus Points

◆ Developing and analyzing visual images for quantities up to 10

◆ Using numbers, and/or addition no tation, to describe arrangements of objects

◆ Decomposing numbers in different ways

Today's Plan			Materials
ACTIVITY **1** *Quick Images: Square Tiles*	15 MIN	CLASS	• Prepared sheets of chart paper*; square tiles*; small paper cups (optional)
ACTIVITY **2** **Introducing Six Tiles in All**	5–10 MIN	CLASS	• M1* • Square tiles*; paper squares*; glue; coloring materials that match the color of the square tiles
ACTIVITY **3** **Six Tiles in All**	10–15 MIN	INDIVIDUALS	• Materials from Activity 2 • Envelope or folder (optional)
DISCUSSION **4** **Checking In**	5 MIN	CLASS	
SESSION FOLLOW-UP **5** **Practice**			• *Student Math Handbook Flip Chart,* pp. 28, 29

*See *Materials to Prepare,* p. 25.

Classroom Routines

Attendance: How Many Have Counted? Count around the circle as usual but pause several times during the count to ask students how many people have counted so far and how they know. Help students see why the number they say represents the number of students who have counted so far and that the last number represents the total number of students in class today.

ACTIVITY

1 *Quick Images: Square Tiles*

15 MIN   CLASS

Explain that today you will revisit *Quick Images* with square tiles. Give each student a set of about ten square tiles of one color, perhaps in a paper cup.❶

I'm going to show you an arrangement of square tiles. Remember, your job is to look carefully, to try to find a way to remember what it looks like so that when it's covered, you'll be able to see it in your mind and build a copy.

Briefly show students the following image, using six tiles of one color.❷

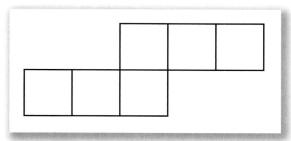

Hide the arrangement from view, and challenge students to use the square tiles in their paper cup to build a copy of it.

Show the arrangement a second time, hide it again, and then give students another minute or two to finish their arrangement.

Finally, unveil the arrangement and let students adjust their work. Then, ask:

What can you tell me about my arrangement? How did you remember what it looked like? How many squares are there in all? How can you tell there are six in all?

Students vary widely in how comfortable they are seeing, remembering, and analyzing visual images. Although some can describe and analyze a mental image they have formed, others find this difficult. Focus the discussion on how they know how many squares there are, rather than just giving the total number of squares.

Some students describe the overall shape or the parts while others mention the total number of squares or the number of squares in each part. If no one uses numbers to describe the arrangement, find opportunities to bring them into the discussion. For example, if students talk about different parts of the picture, ask them about the number of tiles in each part.

Teaching Note

❶ **Preparing to do *Quick Images*** This session is written as if the images are drawn on chart paper and covered with a piece of paper to hide them from view. Other alternatives include cutting out large squares to use on the rug or using transparent square tiles on the overhead projector to display the images.

Math Note

❷ **Why Six?** Six is one of the largest amounts that can be mentally visualized, manipulated, and instantly recalled. Also, because students need more than one hand to represent six on their fingers, they will naturally work with combinations of two numbers (e.g., 6 is 1 and 5, 2 and 4, or 3 and 3).

Professional Development

❸ **Teacher Note:** Introducing Notation in Kindergarten, p. 163

❹ **Dialogue Box:** Pictures and Numbers, p. 184

Tammy says the picture is made of two lines. Can anyone say more about the two lines? . . . Yes, they're both the same size. Who remembers how many squares are in the lines? . . . Kyle remembers three squares in each line. Who remembers something else about the picture?

Record each way that is suggested, emphasizing students' ideas about the number of squares in each part of the picture. For example, sketch the arrangement, circle each part the student mentions, and record the number of squares circled. Recording students' ideas helps them see the different ways to think about the picture and also provides models of how they themselves might record their ideas. Also, use this conversation to introduce and model the use of equations as one way to record.❸ ❹

Repeat this activity once or twice, as time permits, using other arrangements of six tiles:

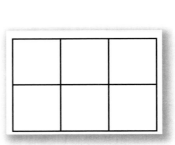 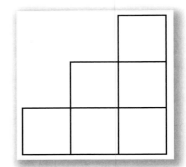

Follow the same process each time:

- Briefly show the arrangement.

- Students use square tiles to make a copy.

- Show the arrangement again.

- Students revise their work.

- Reveal the arrangement. Students describe it and discuss how they remembered what it looked like.

- Use numbers, and addition notation where appropriate, to record the ways students describe the arrangement.

ACTIVITY

2 Introducing Six Tiles in All

5–10 MIN   CLASS

We've been looking at pictures made from six tiles. Now you'll have a chance to make pictures with six tiles.

Remind students of the work they did arranging square tiles in *Measuring and Counting*. Explain that they are going to revisit that activity, but with a new rule. This time, each tile must join the tile next to it along one whole side.

These shapes all fit the rule. Each tile shares one whole side with the tile next to it.

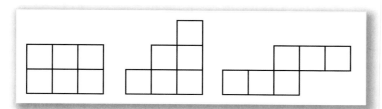

Show four or five additional examples, including some that fit the rule and some that do not. As you show each, ask volunteers to explain whether it fits the rule, and how they know.❺

Does not fit the rule because one square is joined only at a corner.

Fits the rule.

Does not fit the rule because the square on top shares one of its sides with the sides of two different squares.

Does not fit the rule because there is space between the two groups.

Math Note

❺ **Examples and Nonexamples** Showing arrangements that do and do not follow the rule helps students make sense of the new rule, that tiles that touch must share an entire side.

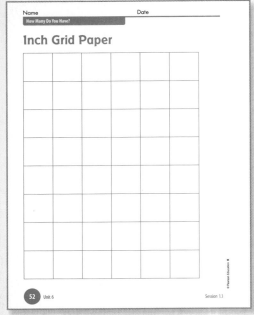

▲ **Student Activity Book, p. 52**
Resource Masters, M1

When you think most students understand the rule, explain that students are to make as many different arrangements of six tiles as they can. Show students the materials they can use to record their arrangements, and explain that each time they make a new arrangement, they should record it. Some students glue down colored paper squares on Inch Grid Paper (M1) or unlined paper. Others prefer to draw their arrangements on grid paper, or to draw or trace their tiles on unlined paper. Remind students who draw in this way that when the class shares their work, you will need to be able to see each square tile in their arrangement.

Students should also show *how they know* their arrangement has six tiles in all. Explain that students may use one of the ways from the *Quick Images* posters or develop their own, but everyone should try to use numbers in their work.

ACTIVITY

③ Six Tiles in All

10–15 MIN   INDIVIDUALS

Students work individually to find different ways to arrange six tiles so that each tile shares an entire side with the tile next to it. They record at least one arrangement to share at the end of class.

ONGOING ASSESSMENT: Observing Students at Work

Students consider many ways to decompose one number, six, into parts.

- **Do students' arrangements follow the rules?** Do they use six tiles? Do tiles that touch share an entire side?

- **How accurately do students record their arrangements of tiles?** Are the parts oriented correctly?

- **How do students record how they know there are six tiles in all?** Do they number each square? Do they circle groups of squares and label the number in each group? Or do they use equations? Do the numbers accurately reflect how many squares are in each group?

Students find different ways to arrange six tiles.

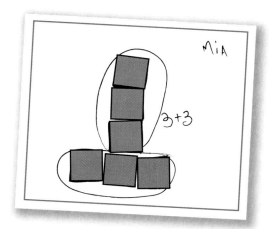

Sample Student Work

DIFFERENTIATION: Supporting the Range of Learners

Intervention Show students who are struggling with the new rule examples of shapes that do and do not fit the rule.

Ask students who just record "6," or who are having difficulty knowing what to record, to show you how they know there are six squares in the drawing. Then, help them find ways to record their strategies. For example, if a student counts each tile:

So, you know there are six because you counted them. What did you say when you counted this tile? What could you write to show that you said "one" for this tile?

Or, if a student points out that there are two in one part and four in another:

You said there are two in this part of the shape and four in this part. How could you show that you saw a group of two and a group of four? How did you know that the group of two and the group of four made six altogether?

Examples of ways to record arrangements with five tiles are included in *Five Tiles* on the *Student Math Handbook Flip Chart* page 27.

5 MIN   CLASS

DISCUSSION

4 Checking In

Take this opportunity to discuss any issues that you noticed while observing students at work. The topic might be mathematical (e.g., using numbers or notation to record) or logistical (e.g., gluing down squares) in nature or relate to a management issue (e.g., sharing square tiles) that arose during the session.

End by asking each student to hold up one arrangement of square tiles that he or she recorded. Encourage students to look at one another's work and comment on anything they notice. If time permits, point out several particular pieces of student work that show different ways to use numbers and addition notation to record.

SESSION FOLLOW-UP

5 Practice

 Student Math Handbook Flip Chart: Use the *Student Math Handbook Flip Chart* pages 28, 29 to reinforce concepts from today's session. See pages 189–193 in the back of this unit.

Toss the Chips

Math Focus Points

- Decomposing numbers in different ways
- Using numbers, and/or addition notation, to describe arrangements of objects and to record how many

Today's Plan		Materials
ACTIVITY **① Introducing** *Toss the Chips*	5 MIN CLASS	• M2* • Two-color counters
MATH WORKSHOP **② Combinations of Six** **2A** *Toss the Chips* **2B** *Six Tiles in All*	15–30 MIN	**2A** • Student Activity Book, p. 53 • Materials from Activity 1 **2B** • Materials from Session 1.1, p. 28
DISCUSSION **③ Arrangements of Six**	10 MIN CLASS	• Square tiles; chart paper
SESSION FOLLOW-UP **④ Homework**		• M3–M4*, Family Letter

*See *Materials to Prepare,* p. 25.

Classroom Routines

Today's Question: Did you have cereal for breakfast today? On chart paper, create a vertical two-column table titled "Did you have cereal for breakfast today?" with "Yes" written at the bottom of one column and "No" written at the bottom of the other column. If students have not already suggested using lines or rows to organize the data, begin to do so now. Draw rows in your table to organize students' responses. As you discuss the result of the survey, ask students how the new table helps them count and compare the data.

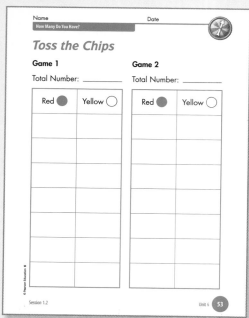

▲ Student Activity Book, p. 53;
   Resource Masters, M2

ACTIVITY

① Introducing *Toss the Chips*

5 MIN   CLASS

Toss the Chips should need only a brief introduction, as students played it in *Measuring and Counting*. Play a few rounds to reintroduce it. Show students a set of 5 two-color counters and ask someone sitting close to you to verify how many counters you have.

I've got five counters in my hand. Remember that these counters are red on one side and yellow on the other. I'm going to drop the chips and see how many land with the red side facing up and how many land with the yellow side facing up.

Toss the counters and ask students what happened.

How many counters landed with the red side facing up? How many counters landed with the yellow side facing up? How many counters are there in all?

Show students how to record this information on *Toss the Chips* (M2). Write "5" on the line next to "Total Number," and record the number of red and yellow in the appropriate boxes in the top row.

If it does not come up naturally, discuss how to record if *all* of the counters land with the red [or yellow] side facing up.

MATH WORKSHOP

② Combinations of Six

15–30 MIN

Explain that two activities are available during Math Workshop. Remind students what each activity entails, what materials are required, and where they are located.

②A *Toss the Chips*

PAIRS   INDIVIDUALS

Students play *Toss the Chips* with 6 two-color counters. They can play individually or in pairs, but each student needs to fill out *Student Activity Book* page 53.

ONGOING ASSESSMENT: Observing Students at Work

Students explore combinations of a number, and use numbers to record.

- **How do students figure out the number of red and yellow?** Can they just see how many of each there are? Do they count? Use one amount to find the other? (For example, "I tossed six and five are red so one is yellow because five and one makes six.")

- **Do students recognize combinations that repeat?**

- **Do students understand that the total number of counters is equivalent to the number of red counters and the number of yellow counters?**

- **Can students use numbers to record?** Can they write the numbers accurately? Do they use zero appropriately?

As you observe, ask students about their work. For example, choose a completed row and ask how many counters they tossed. Then, ask them to show you what that round looked like with two-color counters.

DIFFERENTIATION: Supporting the Range of Learners

 Students who complete one game can play again with a different number of counters. They will need a copy of *Toss the Chips* (M2).

2B Six Tiles in All

INDIVIDUALS

For complete details on this activity, see Session 1.1, pages 31–32.

As you observe, jot down several interesting arrangements of six tiles that students have generated to use in the discussion at the end of this session. Ideally, choose arrangements that several students have made but described in different ways (three and three, two and two and two, and one and two and three).

DISCUSSION

3 Arrangements of Six

10 MIN   CLASS

Math Focus Points for Discussion

◆ Using numbers, and/or addition notation, to describe arrangements of objects

Spend the end of this session discussing several arrangements of six tiles, and gathering different ways to use numbers, and equations where appropriate, to show that there are six.

Choose an arrangement of six tiles that several children have created but described differently. Draw the arrangement on chart paper (or use large paper squares or overhead tiles on the overhead projector) to present the arrangement to the class.

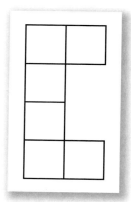

Here is one arrangement of six tiles that I saw several people make. Take a minute to look at this arrangement. How would you describe it? How could you prove that it has six tiles in all? How could you use numbers to show that it has six?

After students have had time to consider the arrangement, ask a volunteer to share how he or she saw it.

[Mia] said this arrangement looked like a "C." She saw two and two and two.

Sketch the image on chart paper and model one way to record the way your volunteer saw the image.

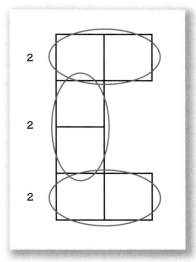

Did anyone else see this arrangement like [Mia]? Who saw it a different way?

Follow the same process with each suggestion, modeling ways to number the squares, label groups of squares, and, where appropriate, write equations that match the way students saw the picture.❶

We had lots of different ways to describe one arrangement of six tiles! [Mia] saw it as two and two and two, [Carmen] saw four and one and one, and [Yoshio] saw three and three.

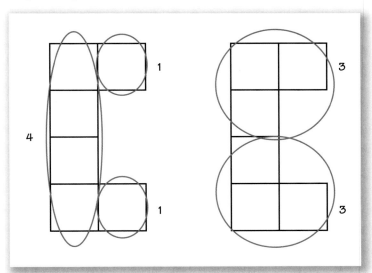

Repeat this process for several arrangements, as time permits.

Math Note

❶ **Using Equations** Be sure to model the correct use of equations. For instance, it is clear what a child who writes $2 + 2 = 4 + 2 = 6$ means: she added 2 and 2 first, and then 2 more to get 6. However, $2 + 2$ is not equivalent to $4 + 2$. This student understands the notation as a sequence of events, rather than as an equation. In this situation record in the following way:

$$2 + 2 = 4$$
$$4 + 2 = 6$$

DIFFERENTIATION: Supporting the Range of Learners

ELL To encourage English Language Learners to participate in this and other discussions, you may want to discuss some tile arrangements with them ahead of time. Have English Language Learners work in pairs to create arrangements of five through ten tiles each. Then ask them to describe their processes, highlighting key vocabulary. How many tiles did you *use*? How do you know? How many tiles are there in this part of your *arrangement*? How many tiles in this part? Let's use numbers to *describe* this arrangement. How can we use numbers to show that this arrangement has [3] tiles in the *top row* and [3] tiles in the *bottom row*?

SESSION FOLLOW-UP

4 Homework

Family Letter: Send home copies of the Family Letter (M3–M4) with each student.

Arrangements of Five Through Ten Tiles

Math Focus Points

◆ Decomposing numbers in different ways

◆ Developing and analyzing visual images for quantities up to 10

◆ Using numbers, and/or addition notation, to describe arrangements of objects and to record how many

Today's Plan		Materials
❶ ACTIVITY **Introducing Arrangements of Five Through Ten Tiles**	🕐 5 MIN CLASS	• Square tiles; chart paper
❷ MATH WORKSHOP **Arrangements of Tiles and Chips** ❷A Arrangements of Five Through Ten Tiles ❷B Toss the Chips	🕐 15–30 MIN	❷A • M5* ☑ • M1* ☑ • Square tiles; paper squares; glue; coloring materials that match the square tiles ❷B • Materials from Session 1.2, p. 35
❸ DISCUSSION **More Tile Arrangements**	🕐 10 MIN CLASS	• Square tiles; chart paper
❹ SESSION FOLLOW-UP **Practice**		• *Student Math Handbook Flip Chart,* pp. 27, 28

*See *Materials to Prepare,* p. 25.

Classroom Routines

Calendar: How Many Days ... ? Students use the calendar to determine how many days until a class event or holiday that will happen this month. Discuss students' strategies for determining the number of days.

ACTIVITY

1 Introducing Arrangements of Five Through Ten Tiles

5 MIN   CLASS

Explain that today students can make arrangements for any of the numbers from 5 through 10. The arrangements need to follow the same rules—each tile needs to share an entire side with the tile next to it.

Show students a set of seven tiles and ask them to think for a moment about how they might arrange them. Ask a volunteer to share an idea with the class.

Here is [Russell's] way. Does it follow the rule? Do all of the tiles share a whole side? How many tiles are in [Russell's] arrangement? How do you know? How could we use numbers to describe [Russell's] arrangement?

Sketch the arrangement of tiles on chart paper, and model the ways students suggest.

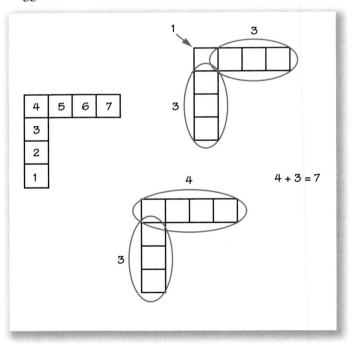

Once students understand the task, explain what is expected of them.

Your job over the next few days is to find different ways to arrange different numbers of tiles. You can make and record as many arrangements as you like, but you need to record *at least two* arrangements for each number from 5 to 10.

Encourage students to use numbers, and addition notation if they are ready, to describe their recorded arrangements.

 MATH WORKSHOP

Arrangements of Tiles and Chips

15–30 MIN INDIVIDUALS PAIRS

Explain that two activities are available during Math Workshop. Remind students what each activity entails, what materials are required, and where they are located.

2A Arrangements of Five Through Ten Tiles

INDIVIDUALS

Students work individually to find different ways to arrange sets of square tiles. They use numbers and/or equations to record at least two arrangements for each number 5 through 10.

ONGOING ASSESSMENT: Observing Students at Work

Students decompose numbers into parts and use numbers, and/or addition notation, to describe arrangements of tiles.❶ ❷

- **Do students' arrangements follow the rules?** Do they use the correct number of tiles? Do they follow the rule that tiles that touch must share an entire side?

- **Can students accurately record an arrangement on grid paper?**

- **How do students describe their arrangements?** Do they number each square? Do they circle groups of squares and label the number in each group? Do they use equations? Do the numbers accurately reflect how many squares are in each group?

DIFFERENTIATION: Supporting the Range of Learners

Intervention Ask students who are struggling with the recording aspect of this task to describe their arrangements aloud. Then, model how they could use numbers (and notation, where appropriate) in ways that match how they "see" their arrangements.

Extension Challenge students to figure out how to make a set that does not have the right number of tiles into one that does, or an arrangement that does not fit the rule into one that does.

Teaching Notes

❶ **Assessing Students as They Write the Numbers** By the end of this unit, students are expected to be able to write the numbers to 10 (Benchmark 1). This means that, given an amount (00000) or a number name (five), they know or can figure out the representative numeral (5), and that they can write it. Students are asked to use numbers to record throughout this Investigation and unit. Use M5 to keep track of your observations as they do so.

❷ **Assembling a Portfolio** As you observe students making and recording tile arrangements, choose one or more examples to include in their portfolios. Because *Measuring and Counting* included a similar activity without such an explicit focus on using numbers and notation to describe arrangements, having work from both units will provide a picture of their growth over time.

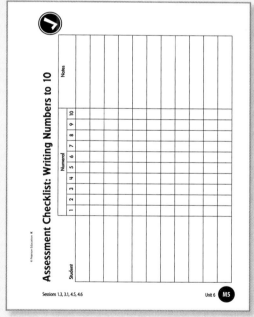

▲ Resource Masters, M5 ☑

2B Toss the Chips

INDIVIDUALS PAIRS

For complete details on this activity, see Session 1.2, page 36.

DIFFERENTIATION: Supporting the Range of Learners

Extension Students who are ready for more of a challenge can play with more counters. You can also challenge them to look over a completed gameboard to see whether they think it shows *all* of the possible combinations of red and yellow counters. Challenge them to find any combinations that are missing and to think about how they know whether they have found them all.

Assessment Checklist: Writing Numbers to 10

Student	Numeral										Notes
	1	2	3	4	5	6	7	8	9	10	
Sarah	✓	✓	R/	R/	✓	/					Toss the Chips
Dennis	✓	✓	R/	✓	R/	✓	✓	✓	✓	✓	Tiles
Mitchell	✓	R/	R/	✓	✓	R/	✓	✓	R/	✓	Tiles
Kaitlyn	✓	✓	✓	✓	✓	✓					Chips
Kyle	✓	✓	✓	✓	✓	✓	R/	✓	✓	R/	Tiles

3 DISCUSSION
More Tile Arrangements

10 MIN CLASS

Math Focus Points for Discussion

◆ Using numbers, and/or addition notation, to describe arrangements of objects

As you did at the end of Session 1.2 and at the beginning of this session, choose a common tile arrangement that can be described differently and present it to the class. Ask students how they see the image and then gather different ways to use numbers, and equations where appropriate, to describe it.

Take a minute to look at this arrangement. How would you describe it? How many tiles are in it? How do you know? How could you prove that it has [#] tiles in all? How could you use numbers to show that it has [#]?

Sketch the image on chart paper and model different ways to record how students see the arrangement. For example, you might number each square for students who count them one by one, circle and label groups of squares, and, when it matches a student's thinking, write an addition equation.

SESSION FOLLOW-UP

Practice

Student Math Handbook Flip Chart: Use the *Student Math Handbook Flip Chart* pages 27, 28 to reinforce concepts from today's session. See pages 189–193 in the back of this unit.

Counting Jar

Math Focus Points

◆ Using numbers, and/or addition notation, to describe arrangements of objects and to record how many

◆ Developing strategies for accurately counting and keeping track of quantities up to 20

◆ Creating an equivalent set

Today's Plan		Materials
DISCUSSION ❶ **More Tile Arrangements** 10 MIN CLASS		• Square tiles; chart paper
MATH WORKSHOP ❷ **Counting and Arranging** ❷Ⓐ The Counting Jar ❷Ⓑ Arrangements of Five Through Ten Tiles ❷Ⓒ *Toss the Chips* 15–30 MIN		❷Ⓐ • M6* ☑ • Counting Jar*; materials for doing the Counting Jar routine (as you have set it up) ❷Ⓑ • Materials from Session 1.3, p. 41; recorded tile arrangements (from Sessions 1.1, 1.2, and 1.3) ❷Ⓒ • Materials from Session 1.2, p. 35
DISCUSSION ❸ **Checking In** 5 MIN CLASS		
SESSION FOLLOW-UP ❹ **Practice**		• *Student Math Handbook Flip Chart,* pp. 20, 27, 28

*See *Materials to Prepare,* p. 27.

Classroom Routines

Attendance: What If We Start With . . . ? As usual, count around the circle to determine the total number of students present today. Then ask students what they think would happen if the count began with a different student and why. Choose a different student to start, count again, and discuss what happens.

1 Discussion | 2 Math Workshop | 3 Discussion | 4 Session Follow-Up

DISCUSSION

More Tile Arrangements

10 MIN   CLASS

Math Focus Points for Discussion

◆ Using numbers, and/or addition notation, to describe arrangements of objects

Choose a common tile arrangement that can be described differently, and present it to the class. Ask students how they see the image and then gather different ways to use numbers, and equations where appropriate, to describe it.

Take a minute to look at this arrangement. How would you describe it? How many tiles are in it? How do you know? How could you show that it has [8] tiles in all? How could you use numbers to show that it has [8]?

Sketch the image on chart paper and model different ways to record how different students see the arrangement. For example, you might number each square for students who count them one by one, circle and label groups of squares, and, when it matches a student's thinking, write an addition equation.

MATH WORKSHOP

Counting and Arranging

15–30 MIN

Show students the Counting Jar with 20 objects in it. Explain that three activities are available during this Math Workshop, and that this is the last day that *Toss the Chips* will be available for a while. Remind students what each activity entails, what materials are required, and where they are located.

2A The Counting Jar

INDIVIDUALS

Students count the objects in the Counting Jar—20 objects. They make a set of the same size and then find a way to record what they found out.

Teaching Note

❶ **Assessing Students' Counting** By the end of this unit, students are expected to be able to count a set of 20 objects accurately (Benchmark 2). This means that they know the number names in sequence, say one number for each object, and have a system for keeping track of what they are counting. Use this activity to get a sense of where students are with these ideas and to plan for Investigation 2, which focuses on counting to 20. (A discussion about this Counting Jar, and the sequence of numbers to 20, happens in the first session of Investigation 2.) You can jot notes on Assessment Checklist: Counting (M6).

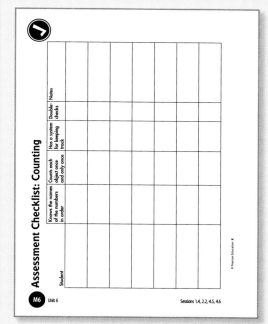

▲ Resource Masters, M6 ☑

Session 1.4 | Counting Jar   **47**

Teaching Notes

❷ Assembling a Portfolio Because students do Counting Jar in every unit, it provides an opportunity to see students' growth over time. Therefore, have students record their work for one of the two Counting Jars in this unit (introduced in this session and in Session 2.6) on a sheet of paper you can collect and put in their portfolio.

❸ Making a Class Book After this session, begin looking through students' work to find and record all of the different ways students have found to arrange each number of tiles. For example, look through students' arrangements of 5 and draw one of each shape on a large sheet of paper titled "Ways to Make 5." (If you use chart grid paper, you can color in squares instead of drawing them.) While two congruent shapes, oriented differently, can look quite different, if a shape can be cut out and laid exactly on top of another shape, they are considered congruent or the same.

Ways to Make 5

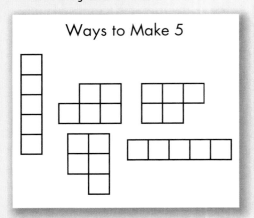

ONGOING ASSESSMENT: Observing Students at Work

Students count a set of objects, create an equivalent set, and record their work.❷

- **How do students count the objects in the jar?** Do they organize the objects in any way? Do they know the sequence of number names? Do they count each item once and only once? Do they double-check?

- **How do students create an equivalent set?** Do they think, "The Counting Jar had 20? I need 20 tiles. 1, 2, 3 . . ."? Do they recreate the Counting Jar set, matching them 1 to 1? Do they double-check?

- **How do students record their work?**

❷Ⓑ Arrangements of Five Through Ten Tiles

INDIVIDUALS

For complete details on this activity, see Session 1.3, pages 42–43.❸

❷Ⓒ *Toss the Chips*

INDIVIDUALS   PAIRS

For complete details on this activity, see Session 1.2, page 36.

DISCUSSION

③ Checking In

5 MIN   CLASS

Take this opportunity to discuss any issues that you noticed while observing students at work. The topic might be mathematical in nature, such as a strategy you would like all students to consider (e.g., grouping or organizing objects to count them), or a common error or misconception you would like students to discuss (e.g., recording just the total number of tiles in an arrangement).

It could also be a logistical issue (e.g., reminding students of the steps involved in the Counting Jar activity) or a management issue (e.g., noise level, making choices and working productively during Math Workshop).

Other alternatives include checking in with students about which activities they have been choosing (e.g., "Thumbs up if you worked on Arranging Tiles today. Thumbs up if you played *Toss the Chips.* Thumbs up if you visited the Counting Jar."), asking everyone to hold up a piece of work, or allowing students to raise a question or make a comment about today's math class.

SESSION FOLLOW-UP

Practice

Student Math Handbook Flip Chart: Use the *Student Math Handbook Flip Chart* pages 20, 27, 28 to reinforce concepts from today's session. See pages 189–193 in the back of this unit.

Racing Bears

Math Focus Points

◆ Counting spaces and moving on a gameboard

◆ Thinking strategically about moves on a gameboard

◆ Decomposing numbers in different ways

Today's Plan			Materials
ACTIVITY **❶ Introducing** *Racing Bears*	🕐 10 MIN	👥 CLASS	• M8* • 1-to-6 dot cubes; teddy bear or other counters; other small counters such as buttons and pennies
ACTIVITY **❷ Playing** *Racing Bears*	🕐 10–25 MIN	👥 PAIRS	• *Student Activity Book,* p. 54 • Materials from Activity 1
DISCUSSION **❸ Racing Bears**	🕐 10 MIN	👥 CLASS	• M8* • Materials from Activity 1
SESSION FOLLOW-UP **❹ Practice**			• *Student Math Handbook Flip Chart,* pp. 27, 28

*See *Materials to Prepare,* p. 27.

Classroom Routines

Patterns on the Pocket Chart: Wraparound Patterns Arrange an AAB repeating pattern on the first two rows of the pocket chart, using 14 or more pattern blocks (red trapezoid, red trapezoid, tan rhombus). Cover the 8th through the last pattern block with Question Mark Cards (M7). Follow the basic *Patterns* activity. Students hold up the pattern block they think is under each Question Mark Card.

ACTIVITY

1 Introducing *Racing Bears*

10 MIN   CLASS

Remind students that they played *Racing Bears* in *Measuring and Counting*, and explain that today they will play with a 1-to-6 dot cube instead of a 1-to-3 dot cube. Set up the *Racing Bears* Gameboard (M8) and review the goal of the game.

Remember that, when you play *Racing Bears,* you and your partner are working together to collect 10 [buttons] in all. When a [bear] lands on a [button], you and your partner get to take that [button] and keep it.

Students set up their gameboard to play
Racing Bears.

Then play a few rounds with a volunteer to introduce the new dot cube and to remind students of the rules of the game. Ask your volunteer to roll the dot cube.

What did [Cindy] roll? How many spaces can she move? How do you know?

Ask your volunteer to choose a bear and move that number of spaces.

Now it's my turn. What did I roll? How many spaces can I move? Remember, I can move *any* of the bears; the one that [Cindy] just moved, or a different one.

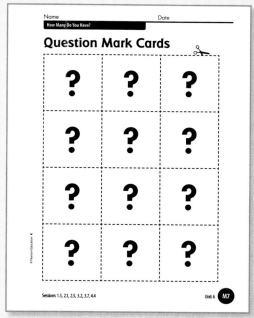

▲ **Resource Masters, M7**

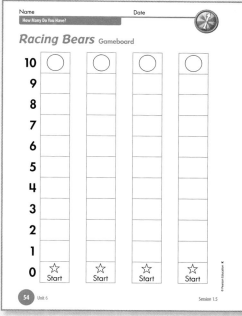

▲ **Student Activity Book, p. 54; Resource Masters, M8**

Choose a bear and move that number of spaces. Continue taking turns. As one or more of the bears nears the end of its track, ask students to decide which bear to move in order to land on a counter.

[Cindy] just rolled a [3]. Remember, our goal is to land on a [button] so that we can collect it. Look carefully at our gameboard. Which bear do you think we should move? Is there a [bear] we could move that would let us capture a [button]?

Remind students that once a counter is captured or collected, players should put the bear back at the beginning of the track, and place a new counter in the circle. Also remind them that players can split a roll and move more than one bear in a turn. For example, if a player rolls a 3 and the red bear is on the eighth space of its track, the player can move the red bear two spaces to get a counter and then move another bear one additional space. If this situation does not arise naturally, use one of your turns to demonstrate what happens when you roll a number that would take a particular bear past the tenth space.

I rolled a 3, but I want to move the yellow bear, which is two spaces from the end. (Move the yellow bear the two spaces.) I rolled 3, and I moved 2. How many moves do I have left? How do you know?

Students count moves on the Racing Bears *Gameboard.*

You might want to demonstrate this type of move several times, because playing with a 1-to-6 dot cube will provide more opportunities for these sorts of moves.

Play several rounds, asking students to explain how they figured out how many spaces to move, how they decided which bear to move, and how they counted the spaces moved. Remind students that the game is over when the players together have collected 10 counters.

ACTIVITY

② Playing *Racing Bears*

10–25 MIN PAIRS

Pairs take turns rolling a dot cube to move teddy bear counters along four tracks of 10 on *Student Activity Book* page 54. The goal is to land on, and thereby capture, the counters on the tenth spaces. The game is over when players have together collected 10 counters.

ONGOING ASSESSMENT: Observing Students at Work

Students practice counting and moving on a game board.

- **Do students recognize the dot patterns?** Or, do they count the dots to determine the number of spaces to move?

- **Do they move the correct number of spaces?** Do they say one and only one number for each space they move along the track?

- **How do students choose which bear to move?** Do they review their options? Do they figure out how many more spaces a bear has to go to land on 10?

- **How do students handle rolls that would take a bear past 10?**

Watch for students who are splitting rolls as they play, to inform the discussion at the end of this session.

DIFFERENTIATION: Supporting the Range of Learners

Intervention Adjust the rules for students who are having difficulty with rolls that take a bear past the tenth space. Tell these students that when a bear reaches the tenth space, whether or not there are leftovers from the roll, that is the end of a turn.

Teaching Note

① **Playing Cooperatively** You may need to reiterate that *Racing Bears* is a cooperative game—students are working together to move the bears and collect the counters rather than playing against each other. In this game, players "win" when they have collected 10 together.

Teaching Notes

❷ Non-mathematical Reasons Some students suggest moving a bear because it is their favorite color or favorite bear. Encourage students to think mathematically and strategically by asking if this will help them collect as many counters as possible.

❸ Preparing for Session 1.6 Before Session 1.6, sort through students' arrangements of 5, 6, and 7 tiles. Prepare a page for each number, showing the different ways students found to arrange those numbers of tiles. (You will need pages for 8, 9, and 10 for Session 1.7.)

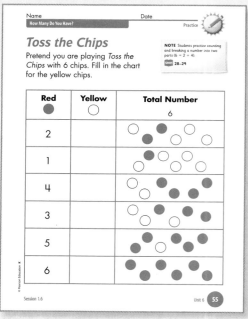

▲ Student Activity Book, p. 55

DISCUSSION

③ Racing Bears

10 MIN   CLASS

Math Focus Points for Discussion

◆ Thinking strategically about moves on a gameboard

Set up a sample game with bears at various locations on the tracks. Place one or two close to the end of a track and one or two more toward the middle. Gather students so they can see the gameboard.

Suppose I am in the middle of playing *Racing Bears* with [Ricardo] and this is where all the bears are. Remember we are trying to collect as many [buttons] as we can.

Roll the dot cube.

I rolled a [4]. Which bear do you think I should move? Why do you think so?

Some suggest moving a bear that is close to the end of one track, in order to get it closer to the end. Others notice when a bear is the same number of spaces from a counter as the amount you rolled and suggest moving that bear so you can collect the counter. Still others see when they can split up a roll and suggest moving more than one bear in order to collect one or more counters.

Try each strategy that students suggest as you play together with the class. Encourage strategic thinking by asking, each time, whether the suggested move will help them collect as many counters as possible.❷ ❸

SESSION FOLLOW-UP

④ Practice

Student Math Handbook Flip Chart: Use the *Student Math Handbook Flip Chart* pages 27, 28 to reinforce concepts from today's session. See pages 189–193 in the back of this unit.

Arranging Five Tiles

Math Focus Points

- Decomposing numbers in different ways
- Using numbers, and/or addition notation, to describe arrangements of objects and to record how many
- Developing and analyzing visual images for quantities up to 10

Today's Plan		Materials
ACTIVITY **① Introducing the Class Book**	5 MIN · CLASS	• Pages for 5, 6, and 7 of the class book, *Ways to Make Numbers***
MATH WORKSHOP **② Counting, Arranging, and Racing** **2A** *Racing Bears* **2B** Counting Jar **2C** Arrangements of Five Through Ten Tiles	20–35 MIN	**2A** • Materials from Session 1.5, p. 50 • 1-to-3 dot cubes (optional) **2B** • Materials from Session 1.4, p. 46 **2C** • Materials from Session 1.3, p. 41 • Pages for 5, 6, and 7 of the class book, *Ways to Make Numbers**; connecting cubes (optional)
DISCUSSION **③ Checking In**	5 MIN · CLASS	• The "5" page of the class book, *Ways to Make Numbers*
SESSION FOLLOW-UP **④ Practice**		• *Student Activity Book*, p. 55 • *Student Math Handbook Flip Chart*, pp. 28–29

*See *Materials to Prepare*, p. 27.

Classroom Routines

Today's Question: Would you rather see a dinosaur or walk on the moon? **On chart paper, create a vertical two-column table with rows drawn in, titled "Would you rather see a dinosaur or walk on the moon?" with the label "Dinosaur" written at the bottom of one column and "Moon" written at the bottom of the other column. Students respond by writing their names in the appropriate column. As you discuss the results of the survey, ask students how the new table helps them count and compare the data.**

Math Note

❶ What Qualifies as Different? While two congruent shapes, oriented differently, can look quite different, if a shape can be cut out and laid exactly on top of another shape, they are considered congruent or the same.

ACTIVITY

5 MIN CLASS

① Introducing the Class Book

Post the pages you have created for the numbers 5, 6, and 7, and explain how you created them.

The other day, I went through all of your work, and looked at all of the ways you found to arrange 5, 6, and 7 tiles. I tried to find all of the *different* ways I could.

Explain what you mean by different, perhaps with a 1-by-5 array of squares.

Some people made a line of five squares like this, going across the page. Some people made a line of five squares, standing like a tower.

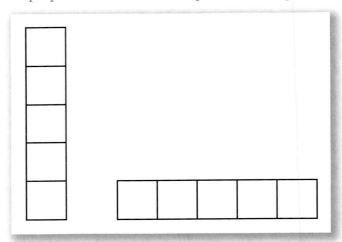

If I could cut out a shape, and turn or move it and put it exactly on top of another shape, then I would say that they were *the same.* ❶

Explain that during Math Workshop, students who have found and recorded two different ways for each number may want to see if they can find any *additional* ways to arrange 5, 6, or 7 tiles.

MATH WORKSHOP

20–35 MIN

② Counting, Arranging, and Racing

Explain that three activities are available during Math Workshop. Remind students what each activity entails, what materials are required, and where they are located.

②A *Racing Bears*

PAIRS

For complete details on this activity, see Session 1.5, pages 51–53.

DIFFERENTIATION: Supporting the Range of Learners

Extension Encourage students who are easily determining the number of dots on the number cube and quickly moving the bears on the board by asking them to play more strategically, perhaps splitting rolls to capture two chips instead of one. Students who are on the edge of being able to split rolls may benefit from playing with a 1-to-3 dot cube instead of a 1-to-6 dot cube.

②B Counting Jar

INDIVIDUALS

For complete details on this activity, see Session 1.4, page 47.

②C Arrangements of Five Through Ten Tiles

INDIVIDUALS

For complete details on this activity, see Session 1.3, pages 42–43.

DIFFERENTIATION: Supporting the Range of Learners

Extension Students who have created and recorded two arrangements of square tiles for each number from 5 through 10 can try to find ways to arrange 5, 6, or 7 tiles that are not yet on your poster. They could also help you work on pages for the numbers 8, 9, and 10.

Or, challenge them to find different ways to arrange connecting cubes, a material that presents 3-D possibilities. Suggest that they start with six cubes.

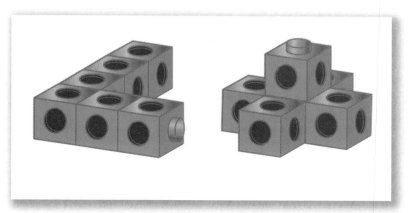

Teaching Note

❶ **Preparing for Session 1.7** Before Session 1.7, sort through students' arrangement of 8, 9, and 10 tiles. Prepare a page for each number, showing the different ways students found to arrange those numbers of tiles.

Math Note

❷ **But I Had One That's Not Up There!** Many Kindergarten students see shapes that are congruent, but oriented differently, as different. Explain how you decided whether a shape was different, perhaps demonstrating with a 1 × 5 rectangle, but acknowledge how different that shape can look when arranged horizontally, vertically, or diagonally. Do not expect all kindergarteners to agree on what makes a shape the same or different.

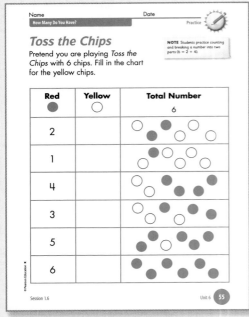

▲ Student Activity Book, p. 55

DISCUSSION

③ Checking In

5 MIN   CLASS

Display the page you made of the different ways students found to arrange five tiles.❶

These are all of the different ways you found to arrange five square tiles, with the rule being that tiles that touch must share an entire side. What do you notice?

Students often notice and discuss:

• The number of different arrangements represented on the poster

• Shapes that are on the poster that they did not find while they worked

• Shapes that they found that they do not see represented on the poster ❷

• The strategies they used to try to find all of the possible arrangements, for example, making a line of squares and then moving one square methodically around that line

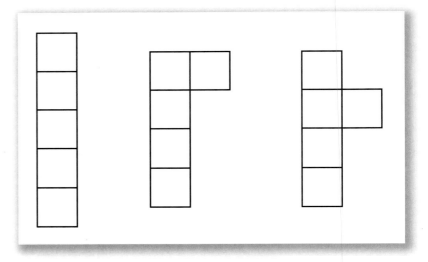

SESSION FOLLOW-UP

④ Practice

Practice: For reinforcement of this unit's content, have students complete *Student Activity Book* page 55.

Arranging Eight Tiles

Math Focus Points

◆ Decomposing numbers in different ways

◆ Using numbers, and/or addition notation, to describe arrangements and to record how many

◆ Developing and analyzing visual images for quantities up to 10

Today's Plan		Materials
① ACTIVITY **More Pages of the Class Book**	🕐 👥 5 MIN CLASS	• Pages for 8, 9, and 10 of the class book, *Ways to Make Numbers**
② MATH WORKSHOP **Counting, Arranging, and Racing** **2A** *Racing Bears* **2B** Counting Jar **2C** Arrangements of Five Through Ten Tiles	🕐 25–35 MIN	**2A** • Materials from Session 1.5, p. 50 **2B** • Materials from Session 1.4, p. 46 **2C** • Materials from Session 1.3, p. 41 • Pages for 8, 9, and 10 of the class book, *Ways to Make Numbers**
③ DISCUSSION **Checking In**	🕐 👥 5 MIN CLASS	• The "8" page of the class book, *Ways to Make Numbers**
④ SESSION FOLLOW-UP **Practice**		• *Student Math Handbook Flip Chart,* pp. 27, 28

*See *Materials to Prepare,* p. 27.

Classroom Routines

Calendar: What's Missing? Remove two days-of-the-week cards from the monthly calendar. Challenge students to tell you which cards are missing and how they know.

ACTIVITY

5 MIN   **CLASS**

More Pages of the Class Book

Post the pages you have created for the numbers 8, 9, and 10. Remind students about how you created them and how you decided which shapes were different.

Explain that some students may want to see whether they can find any *additional* ways to arrange eight, nine, or ten tiles during Math Workshop.

MATH WORKSHOP

25–35 MIN

Counting, Arranging, and Racing

Explain that three activities are available during Math Workshop and that today is the last day Arrangements of Five Through Ten Tiles will be available. Remind students what each activity entails, what materials are required, and where they are located.

2A Racing Bears

PAIRS

For complete details about this activity, see Session 1.5, pages 51–53.

2B Counting Jar

INDIVIDUALS

For complete details about this activity, see Session 1.4, page 47.

2C Arrangements of Five Through Ten Tiles

INDIVIDUALS

For complete details about this activity, See Session 1.3, pages 42–43.

DIFFERENTIATION: Supporting the Range of Learners

Extension Ask students who need more challenge to try to find ways to arrange eight, nine, or ten tiles that are not yet on your poster.

Another way to extend the work with tiles is to ask all students to choose one arrangement of, for example, 6, and use an equation to describe it. (Some students may need help translating their work into an equation.) Then, sort and post those arrangements onto posters that each have the same label (e.g., 1 + 5, 3 + 3, 2 + 2 + 2).

DISCUSSION

Checking In

5 MIN   CLASS

As you did at the end of Session 1.6, display the page you made of the different ways students found to arrange eight tiles. ❶

These are all of the different ways you found to arrange eight square tiles, following the rule that tiles that touch must share an entire side. What do you notice?

Students often notice and discuss the following:

- The number of different arrangements represented on the poster

- Shapes on the poster that they did not find while they worked

- Shapes they found, but that they do not see on the poster

- The strategies they used to try to find all of the possible arrangements; for example, making a line of squares and then moving one square methodically around that line

SESSION FOLLOW-UP

Practice

Student Math Handbook Flip Chart: Use the *Student Math Handbook Flip Chart* pages 27, 28 to reinforce concepts from today's session. See pages 189–193 in the back of this unit.

Teaching Note

❶ **Making a Big Book** After Session 1.7, bind the pages into a class big book about *Ways to Make Numbers*. As you put the book together and read through it as a class, interesting conversations can take place. For example, why are there relatively few ways to show 5 and so many ways to show 10?

Mathematical Emphases

Counting and Quantity Developing strategies for accurately counting a set of objects by ones

Math Focus Points

◆ Developing strategies for accurately counting and keeping track of quantities up to 20

◆ Using subsets to count a set of objects

Whole Number Operations Making sense of and developing strategies to solve addition and subtraction problems with small numbers

Math Focus Points

◆ Finding the total after 1, 2, or 3 is added to, or subtracted from, a set

Whole Number Operations Using manipulatives, drawings, tools, and notation to show strategies and solutions

Math Focus Points

◆ Using numbers, pictures, and/or words to represent a quantity or measurement

This Investigation also focuses on

◆ Repeating multiple nonstandard units to quantify length

Counting and Measuring

	Student Activity Book	Student Math Handbook Flip Chart	Professional Development: Read Ahead of Time
SESSION 2.1 p. 68			
Collect 15 Together Students play *Collect 15 Together*, a version of *Collect 10 Together* that provides practice with counting to 15. Class discussion focuses on the Counting Jar, which contains 20 objects.		12, 19	• **Teacher Note:** Counting Is More Than 1, 2, 3, p. 166; Observing Kindergarteners as They Count, p. 165
SESSION 2.2 p. 74			
Inventory Bags Students have inventory bags of related items, such as markers, pencils, and crayons. They find out how many items in all and how many of each kind of item are in the bag and make a representation that shows their results.	56	12, 13, 19	
SESSION 2.3 p. 79			
Measuring Ourselves Students are introduced to an activity which involves measuring length and counting larger sets of objects. In Measuring Ourselves, students use cubes to measure the length of various body parts (i.e., head, legs, hands, arms). Math Workshop focuses on developing strategies for accurate counting to 20.	57	19, 38	• **Teacher Note:** Learning About Length: Lining Up Units, p. 167
SESSION 2.4 p. 83			
Do We Have to Count Them All? Class begins with a discussion about counting. Math Workshop continues to focus on developing strategies for accurate counting to 20.		12, 13, 19	

Classroom Routines See page 20 for an overview.

Patterns on the Pocket Chart
- Pocket Chart(s)
- M7, Question Mark Cards (from Investigation 1)
- Prepared cups or bags of square tiles
- Prepared cups or bags of pattern blocks

Attendance
- Attendance Stick

Today's Question
- Today's Question chart for Session 2.3.
  See instructions on page 79.

Calendar
- Class calendar or pocket calendar

Materials to Gather	Materials to Prepare
• **Pennies or other counters** (20 per pair) • **Materials for** *Racing Bears* See Session 1.5. • **Materials for Counting Jar** See Session 1.4.	• **M9, Fifteen-Frame** Make copies. (as needed) • **1-to-3 dot cubes** Cover the 4, 5, and 6 sides of a regular dot cube with stick-on dots that have 1, 2, and 3 dots drawn on them. (If you taught *Measuring and Counting*, you already prepared a class set of 1-to-3 cubes.) (1 per pair)
• **Prepared Inventory Bags** (7–10 per class) • **Materials for** *Collect 15 Together* See Session 2.1.	• **M10, Inventory Bag** Make copies. (as needed) • **M11, Ten-Frame** Make copies. (as needed) If you prepared cardstock or laminated Ten-Frames in Unit 4, you may use them in this unit. • **Inventory Bags** Place sets of 10–20 related items in 7–10 bags and label each bag with a letter. Choose items that fall into clear categories such as things to write with (markers, pencils, and crayons), things to eat with (plastic forks, knives, and spoons), pattern blocks of different shapes, or connecting cubes or color tiles in four different colors. Make an answer key showing how many of each item you put in each bag.
• **Connecting cubes** • **Materials for Inventory Bags** See Session 2.2. • **Materials for** *Collect 20 Together* See Session 2.2.	
• **Materials for Measuring Ourselves** See Session 2.3. • **Materials for Inventory Bags** See Session 2.2. • **Materials for** *Collect 20 Together* See Session 2.2.	

☑ Checklist Available

Counting and Measuring,
continued

	Student Activity Book	Student Math Handbook Flip Chart	Professional Development: Read Ahead of Time	
SESSION 2.5 p. 87				
How Did You Count? Class begins with a discussion about how students counted the items in one Inventory Bag. Math Workshop continues to focus on developing strategies for accurate counting to 20.		19, 38		
SESSION 2.6 p. 91				
Representing an Inventory A new Counting Jar is added to Math Workshop, which continues to focus on developing strategies for accurate counting to 20. Class discussion focuses on different strategies for representing an inventory.	58		• **Teacher Note:** Assessing Addition, p. 168	

Materials to Gather	Materials to Prepare
• **Materials for Measuring Ourselves** See Session 2.3. • **Materials for Inventory Bags** See Session 2.2. • **Materials for _Collect 20 Together_** See Session 2.2.	
• **Materials for the Counting Jar routine** (as you have set it up) • **Materials for Measuring Ourselves** See Session 2.3. • **Materials for Inventory Bags** See Session 2.2. • **Materials for _Collect 20 Together_** See Session 2.2.	• **M12, Assessment Checklist: Addition** ✓ Make copies. (3–4 per class; plus extras as needed) • **Counting Jar** Place 5 red and 5 blue square tiles in the jar. • **Work Samples** Choose samples of work for the second Inventory Bag you asked all students to do. The work should show the different ways students are recording.

✓ Checklist Available

Collect 15 Together

Math Focus Points

◆ Developing strategies for accurately counting and keeping track of quantities up to 20

◆ Finding the total after 1, 2, or 3 is added to, or subtracted from, a set

Vocabulary

eleven	fifteen	eighteen
twelve	sixteen	nineteen
thirteen	seventeen	twenty
fourteen		

Today's Plan

	Materials
ACTIVITY **① Introducing** *Collect 15 Together* 5 MIN CLASS	• 1-to-3 dot cube*; pennies or other counters
MATH WORKSHOP **② Collecting and Counting** **2A** *Collect 15 Together* **2B** *Racing Bears* **2C** Counting Jar 15–30 MIN	**2A** • M9* • Pennies or other counters; 1-to-3 dot cubes **2B** • Materials from Session 1.5, p. 50 **2C** • Materials from Session 1.4, p. 46
DISCUSSION **③ Counting Jar** 5 MIN CLASS	• Materials from Session 1.4, p. 46
SESSION FOLLOW-UP **④ Practice**	• *Student Math Handbook Flip Chart,* pp. 12, 19

*See *Materials to Prepare,* p. 65.

Classroom Routines

Patterns on the Pocket Chart: Wraparound Patterns Arrange an ABC repeating pattern on the first two rows of the pocket chart using 14 or more pattern blocks (blue rhombus, orange square, green triangle). Cover the eighth through the last pattern block with Question Mark Cards. Follow the basic *Patterns* activity. Students hold up the pattern block that they think is under each Question Mark Card.

ACTIVITY

1 Introducing *Collect 15 Together*

5 MIN   CLASS

Students should need only a brief introduction to this game since they played it (and *Collect 10 Together*) in *Measuring and Counting*. Ask students what they remember about *Collect 15 Together*, and reintroduce it by playing a brief demonstration game.

In *Collect 15 Together*, two players take turns rolling a 1-to-3 dot cube and taking as many pennies as there are dots on the cube. The goal is to collect 15 pennies together.

Ask volunteers to take turns rolling the dot cube. Involve the class in each turn:

What did [Jae] roll? How many pennies should he take? How do you know?

Ask students to observe your volunteers as they count. Encourage them to reflect on strategies for remembering how many pennies there are at the end of each round and on how they know whether your volunteers have 15 pennies yet.

[Jae] rolled a [2], and then [Rebecca] rolled a [3]. Do you think they have 15 pennies yet? Why do you think so? How many do they have? How do you know? Is that more or less than 15? How do you know?

Ask students to show how they find the total and explain how they know whether that number is more or less than 15. Some count from one while others count on.

Students might say:

"There were 2, and 3 more makes 3, 4, 5."

Others use knowledge of addition combinations they know:

"I know that 2 and 3 makes 5."

Where in our classroom could we find out whether [5] is more or less than 15? How else could you compare [5] and 15 to see which is more?

The game is over as soon as players have at least 15 pennies. Depending on the ending roll, they may end up with exactly 15 or with more than 15.

MATH WORKSHOP
Collecting and Counting

15–30 MIN

Explain that three activities are available during Math Workshop. Also remind students that the Counting Jar needs to be completed by the end of this Workshop, as you will discuss it at the end of this session. Also, let students know that today is the last day that *Racing Bears* will be available for a while. (It comes up again in Investigation 4.) Remind students what each activity entails, what materials are required, and where they are located

2A *Collect 15 Together*

PAIRS

Students take turns rolling a 1-to-3 dot cube. The goal is to accumulate 15 pennies.

ONGOING ASSESSMENT: Observing Students at Work

Students count and keep track of a growing set of objects as they work to create a set of a given size, 15.

- **Do students need to count the dots to see how many pennies to take?** Do they take the same number of pennies as dots on the cube?

- **Do students count the pennies accurately?** What sorts of errors do you notice?

- **How do students find the total number of pennies after new ones have been added?** Do they count them from one, or do they count on from the number they had at the end of the last turn? Do they "just know" some combinations that are one (or two, or three) more?

As students play, ask questions that focus on the mathematical ideas in this game:

How many pennies do you have? If that's [7] pennies, and you just rolled a [1], how many do you have now? Do you need to count all of the pennies?

How many more pennies do you think you need to have 15? How do you know?

Some students use the Fifteen-Frame to organize and keep track of the pennies.

DIFFERENTIATION: Supporting the Range of Learners

Intervention Consider playing with students who are having difficulty counting and keeping track of amounts to 15 in a small group.❶ These students may benefit from using a Fifteen-Frame (M9) to organize and keep track of the pennies.

You can also adjust the level of challenge by varying the type of counters students use to play. For example, ask those who have trouble organizing and keeping track of a count to use cubes (which can be linked together) or teddy bear counters or square tiles (which students tend to line up). Students who are fluent with counting can be challenged with materials that are more difficult to organize, such as buttons.

ELL Some English Language Learners may need extra practice to become fluent in the teen counting sequence. You can gather these students informally during Math Workshop and have them review the sequence in various ways: by counting objects, saying the numbers on a 100 chart or number line, or sitting in a circle and

---

Math Note

❶ **The Teen Numbers** The number sequence in the teens is often challenging for students, in part because it does not follow the same pattern as the rest of the numbers. For example, we do not say ten-one, ten-two, ten-three for 11, 12, 13, the same way we say 21, 22, 23 (or 31, 32, 33 or 41, 42, 43). Also, the words *eleven, twelve, thirteen,* and *fifteen* do not give the same clues about the numerals in them that *fourteen, sixteen, seventeen, eighteen,* and *nineteen* do, and some students struggle because two of these numbers begin with the same sound: *fourteen* and *fifteen.* For more information see the **Teacher Notes:** Observing Kindergarteners as They Count, p. 165 and Counting Is More Than 1, 2, 3, p. 166.

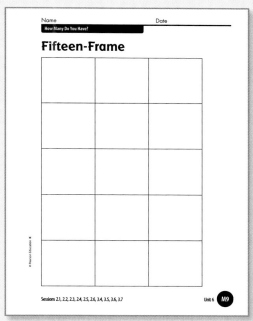

▲ **Resource Masters, M9**

"counting off" to 20. To help English Language Learners learn to read, write, and speak the name of each number, use a set of number cards. Hold up written numbers and ask students to name them, or say the numbers aloud and ask students to write down what they hear or point to the appropriate card.

2B Racing Bears

PAIRS

For complete details on this activity, see Session 1.5, pages 51–53.

2C Counting Jar

INDIVIDUALS

For complete details on this activity, see Session 1.4, page 47.

5 MIN   CLASS

DISCUSSION

3 Counting Jar

Math Focus Points for Discussion

◆ Developing strategies for accurately counting and keeping track of quantities up to 20

Gather students to discuss the Counting Jar. Ask them what they found in the jar and to share anything they noticed about the task this week. As this is the largest amount you have placed in the jar so far this year, students will likely comment on the number of items. If they do not, bring it up yourself.

Look at our Counting Jar this week. [Hold up the jar.] There are a lot of [shells] in there! Did it seem like a lot of [shells]? Did having so many [shells] in the jar make the counting more challenging? Why?

Some students say that it is hard to keep track of such a large group of objects, while others say that the sequence above ten is tricky. If students do not mention these issues, bring them up yourself as you model the counting of the items in the jar.

Okay, I am going to count the [shells]. Watch carefully while I count.

Dump out the Counting Jar, leaving the objects in an unorganized pile. Count them aloud, touching one object for each number you say. After counting ten objects, make mistakes in the number sequence, repeating a number and/or skipping another altogether until students stop you.

1, 2, 3, 4, 5, 6, 7, 8, 9, 10, 12, 13, 13 . . . What? What's the matter? . . . [Tammy] said that I skipped 11, and [Lionel] heard me say 13 twice. These numbers over ten are tricky!

Ask students to help you practice the sequence of numbers to 20. Count together several times with you or a volunteer keeping track of the numbers the class is saying on the number line or class calendar.

Okay, now that we have practiced the numbers over 10, I am going to try to count the [shells] again. Watch carefully.

Again, do not organize the items. Say the sequence correctly this time, but count in a disorganized manner, losing track of what you have counted and what remains to be counted, skipping some and counting others more than once until students stop you.

[Lisa] said she thinks I skipped this one, and [Raul] thinks I counted this one twice. There were so many [shells] that I was getting confused about which ones I had counted and which ones I still had to count. Does anyone have a strategy to help me?

Some students organize the [shells] in groups or a line. Then they count them, beginning at one end and touching one each time they say a number until they reach the end of the line. Others may not organize the [shells] in any way, but pick up and move each shell as they count it. Model, or ask students to model, the strategies that are suggested. Ask the whole class to count aloud with you (or your student volunteer) as you count them.

Russell said he puts them in a line and then counts them in order. Let's try it. So we got 20 when we used Russell's way. What if we try Corey's idea and move each shell as we count it? How many do you think we'll get then? Let's try it.

Some students will recognize that if you are counting the same set of objects, you should get the same total no matter how you count. Others will not yet realize this. For example, many think counting by 1s will result in a different total than counting by 2s. Such questions offer students the chance to think about and test their ideas.

SESSION FOLLOW-UP

 4 Practice

 Student Math Handbook Flip Chart: Use the *Student Math Handbook Flip Chart* pages 12, 19 to reinforce concepts from today's session. See pages 189–193 in the back of this unit.

Inventory Bags

Math Focus Points

- Using subsets to count a set of objects
- Using numbers, pictures, and/or words to represent a quantity
- Finding the total after 1, 2, or 3 is added to, or subtracted from, a set

Today's Plan		Materials
ACTIVITY ① **Introducing Inventory Bags**	10 MIN CLASS	• M10* • Inventory Bag*
MATH WORKSHOP ② **Counting to 20** ②A Inventory Bags ②B *Collect 20 Together*	20–30 MIN	②A • *Student Activity Book,* p. 56 • M10* • Inventory Bags ②B • M11 • Materials from Session 2.1, p. 68
DISCUSSION ③ **Checking In**	5 MIN CLASS	
SESSION FOLLOW-UP ④ **Practice**		• *Student Math Handbook Flip Chart,* pp. 12, 13, 19

*See *Materials to Prepare,* p. 65.

Classroom Routines

Attendance: Comparing Groups Count around the circle as usual, then count the number of students present in class and the number absent from class today. Ask students whether there are more students present or more students absent. Use the *Attendance* Stick to represent the situation and to model students' strategies. Challenge students to figure out how many more and discuss their strategies.

ACTIVITY

① Introducing Inventory Bags

10 MIN   CLASS

In *Counting and Comparing* (Unit 2), students took inventory of bags that contained only one kind of item. Remind students of this work before introducing the new Inventory Bags.

Today we're going to take inventory of the things in another set of Inventory Bags. Here's one of the new bags, Bag C. What kinds of things are in Bag C? [Display the contents of one bag.] There are [markers, crayons, and pencils—things we write with].

Invite volunteers to count the items in the bag, but do not record these amounts.

So, [Abby] counted five markers, [Lionel] counted two crayons, and [Victor] counted four pencils. How could we find out how many things there are in all?

Although most students count all, some may count on, and a few use addition combinations they know. Try each strategy that students suggest.❶

Show students where to record the letter of the bag on Inventory Bag (M10). Then, gather a few ideas about how they might show the results of an inventory.

What did we find out about Inventory Bag C? How could we show that on paper?

Ask two or three students to share their ideas for recording with numbers, pictures, or words, but do not model their suggestions. When a teacher demonstrates one way to record, students tend to use that method rather than developing their own.

Explain that pairs should choose a bag together and then figure out how many of each kind of thing (markers, crayons, pencils) is in the bag, as well as how many items are in the bag altogether. Then, each student needs to find a way to show exactly what was in the bag on their own recording sheets. When they finish, they should return the items to the bag, return the bag to a specified location, and then choose another Inventory Bag.

Also explain that sometime during the week every student should inventory two particular bags (e.g., B and C), for the discussions in Session 2.5 and Session 2.6.

Teaching Note

❶ **Is It 12 or 13?** Because it is likely that pairs will get different numbers when they count, be sure to talk about ways to disagree respectfully. Discuss strategies for resolving such discrepancies, such as carefully recounting or counting in a different way to double-check their answer. When students cannot agree, students' representations should show how many they personally think are in the bag.

▲ **Student Activity Book, p. 56;** **Resource Masters, M10**

Teaching Notes

❷ **Assessing Students' Counting** By the end of this unit, students are expected to be able to count a set of 20 objects (Benchmark 2). This means that they know the number names in sequence, say one number for each object, and have a system for keeping track of what they are counting. Use Assessment Checklist: Counting (M6) to keep track of your observations about students' counting over the course of this unit.

❸ **Assembling a Portfolio** As you observe students at work on Inventory Bags, look for a piece of work to include in their portfolios. Because students did a similar activity in *Measuring and Counting*, including another example will show how students have grown in their ability to count, combine, and represent quantities.

MATH WORKSHOP

② Counting to 20②

 20–30 MIN

Explain that two activities are available during Math Workshop, and that *Collect 20 Together* is a variation on *Collect 15 Together*, with the only difference being that the goal is collecting 20 instead of 15 pennies. Remind students what each activity entails, what materials are required, and where they are located.

2A Inventory Bags

 PAIRS

Pairs inventory sets of related items. Each student records the results on *Student Activity Book* page 56.

ONGOING ASSESSMENT: Observing Students at Work ✓

Students practice counting sets of objects and representing an inventory.❸

- **Do students organize the objects to count them?** How?

- **How do students find the number in each group?** The total number? Do they count from one? Do they count on from the number in one group? Do any combine the numbers in the subsets?

- **How do students show their results?** Do they use pictures? Numbers? Words? Some combination of these? Do any use addition notation? Do their representations show the number in each subgroup as well as the total number of items? The kind of items as well as the number?

Students organize the objects in their Inventory Bag before counting.

DIFFERENTIATION: Supporting the Range of Learners

Intervention Remind students that, because the Inventory Bags contain larger amounts, organizing the objects may be helpful. Some will need support with the names and sequence of the teen numbers; others may need help thinking about ways to record, or reminders about the information a complete representation should include.

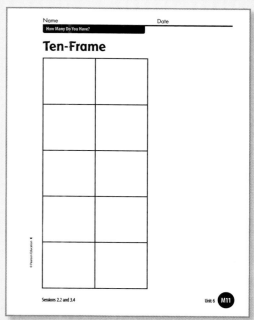

Name _____ **Date** _____

How Many Do You Have?

Ten-Frame

Sessions 2.2 and 3.4   Unit 6 **M11**

▲ Resource Masters, M11

2B *Collect 20 Together*

PAIRS

Students take turns rolling a 1-to-3 dot cube. The goal is to accumulate 20 pennies.

For complete details on this activity, see *Collect 15 Together*, Session 2.1, pages 69–70.

DIFFERENTIATION: Supporting the Range of Learners

Intervention Consider playing in a small group with students who are having difficulty counting and keeping track of amounts to 20 to provide practice with the sequence to 20 and to model strategies for accurately counting and keeping track of a count. Use a variety of different materials as counters, from cubes (which can be linked together) to teddy bear counters or square tiles (which students tend to line up) to pennies or buttons (which are more difficult to organize). Students may benefit from using two Ten-Frames (M11) to organize and keep track of their counters.

Assessment Checklist: Counting

Student	Knows the names of the numbers in order	Counts each object once and only once	Has a system for keeping track	Double-checks	Notes
Cindy	says 14,14,15	✓	✓ (line)	no	Counting jar
Lionel	✓	no, because too many objects but he seems to know this	✓ more slowly		Counting jar
Mia	✓	✓	✓ (touch)	no	Collect 20. Counts on when <10 pennies. >10 pennies, only if rolls a 1.
Manuel	skips 15	✓	✓ (moves)	✓ but gets same # b/c skips 15	Counting jar
Latoya	✓	✓	✓ (moves)	no	Collect 20. Counts from 1 after every roll.

DISCUSSION

③ Checking In

5 MIN   CLASS

Take this opportunity to discuss any issues that you noticed while observing students at work. The topic might be mathematical in nature, such as a strategy you would like all students to consider (e.g., keeping track of a count by moving each object as it is counted or using a number and one picture to record the information about one subset) or a common error or misconception you'd like students to discuss (e.g., omitting or repeating numbers in the sequence of numbers over 10 while counting).

It could also be a logistical issue (e.g., reminding students to record the letter on their bag or reminding students to return their Inventory Bag (with the same number of items they started with) to the agreed upon location) or a management issue (e.g., disagreeing respectfully, being responsible with materials, being a helpful partner).

Other alternatives include asking everyone to hold up a piece of work or allowing students to raise a question or make a comment about today's math class.

SESSION FOLLOW-UP

④ Practice

 Student Math Handbook Flip Chart: Use the *Student Math Handbook Flip Chart* pages 12, 13, 19 to reinforce concepts from today's session. See pages 189–193 in the back of this unit.

Measuring Ourselves

Math Focus Points

◆ Repeating multiple nonstandard units to quantify length

◆ Using numbers, pictures, and/or words to represent a quantity or measurement

◆ Developing strategies for accurately counting and keeping track of quantities up to 20

Vocabulary

length
measure
how long

Today's Plan		Materials
① ACTIVITY **Introducing Measuring Ourselves** 5–10 MIN CLASS		• *Student Activity Book,* p. 57 • Connecting cubes
② MATH WORKSHOP **Counting and Measuring** 20–30 MIN **2A** Measuring Ourselves **2B** Inventory Bags **2C** *Collect 20 Together*		**2A** • *Student Activity Book,* p. 57 • Connecting cubes **2B** • Materials from Session 2.2, p. 74 **2C** • Materials from Session 2.2, p. 74
③ DISCUSSION **Checking In** 5 MIN CLASS		
④ SESSION FOLLOW-UP **Practice**		• *Student Math Handbook Flip Chart,* pp. 19, 38

Classroom Routines

Today's Question: Do you have an older brother? **On chart paper, create a vertical two-column table with rows drawn in titled "Do you have an older brother?" with the heading "Yes" at the bottom of one column and "No" written at the bottom of the other column. Students respond by writing their names in the appropriate column. As you discuss the results of the survey, ask students how the new table helps them count and compare the data.**

Math Note

❶ **What's the Length?** Just as with any measurement situation, discuss and agree upon where your hand begins and ends, and which part of your hand represents the *length*. If the distance across your hand comes up, explain that people consider that the width of your hand, or how wide it is. Reassure students that they will be able to measure both the length and the width of their hands.

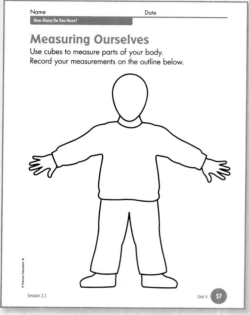

▲ **Student Activity Book, p. 57**

ACTIVITY

5–10 MIN CLASS

1 Introducing Measuring Ourselves

Remind students of the work they did in *Measuring and Counting,* using craft sticks and connecting cubes to measure the length of shoes, classroom objects, and strips of ribbon or tape.

We measured the length of a lot of different things, including a part of ourselves—our foot or shoe. Now we are going to have a chance to measure the length of other parts of our bodies. We're going to answer questions like: how long is your hand? Your arm? Your leg?

Explain that students will be working in partners so they can help each other measure, since it can be challenging to measure parts of yourself.

Suppose [Mary] and I wanted to use cubes to measure the length of my hand? What could we do? ❶

Take a few suggestions and try them out, encouraging students to snap the cubes together as they measure.

So we agreed that my hand is [9] cubes long. How could I show what we found out on this recording sheet?

Some students suggest drawing [nine] cubes. Others suggest writing [9] on the hand or using numbers and arrows.

Explain that students need to measure and record at least four body parts, although they can do more if they wish.

MATH WORKSHOP

20–30 MIN

2 Counting and Measuring

Explain that three activities are available during Math Workshop. Remind students what each activity entails, what materials are required, and where they are located.

2A Measuring Ourselves

PAIRS

Pairs work together to measure the length of different parts of their bodies and record their results on *Student Activity Book* page 57.

ONGOING ASSESSMENT: Observing Students at Work

Students line up units and count a set of cubes to measure length.❷

- **How do students use cubes to measure the length of a body part?** Do they make a cube tower that is approximately the same length as the body part?❸

- **How do students count the cubes?** What errors do you notice? At what point in the sequence?

- **How do students record their measurements?**

Professional Development

❷ **Teacher Note:** Learning About Length: Lining Up Units, p. 167

Teaching Note

❸ **Measuring Accurately?** Measuring a body part (e.g., an arm) is more difficult than measuring an object with clear dimensions (e.g., a book or box). Therefore, do not expect students to measure accurately. Instead, use this activity to provide further practice with determining what length is by lining up units to measure length, and by comparing lengths (of body parts and cube towers).

Student measuring partner's hand with connecting cubes.

DIFFERENTIATION: Supporting the Range of Learners

Intervention Encourage students who find counting amounts to 20 challenging to focus on shorter lengths. However, many students will want to measure their height. This is fine, as students need exposure to, and practice with, the rote sequence to higher numbers in order to begin to learn and see the patterns in this sequence. Although accuracy is the goal when counting, do not expect your students to accurately count such large amounts. Encourage students to count together and double-check their answers. Support them by counting together and modeling the use of the number line as a tool for counting.

2B Inventory Bags

PAIRS

For complete details on this activity, see Session 2.2, page 75.

. . . .

2C *Collect 20 Together*

PAIRS

For complete details on this activity, see Session 2.2, page 77.

DIFFERENTIATION: Supporting the Range of Learners

Extension Students who are ready for more challenge can roll two 1-to-3 dot cubes. They may use one or both of the numbers that are rolled, the goal being to collect 20 exactly.

DISCUSSION

3 Checking In

5 MIN   CLASS

Take this opportunity to discuss any issues that you noticed while observing students at work. The topic might be mathematical in nature, such as a strategy you would like all students to consider (e.g., one partner touching each cube while the other keeps track of the numbers on the number line, a strategy for recording a measurement) or a common error or misconception you would like students to discuss (e.g., skipping or double counting objects, or omitting or repeating numbers while counting).

It could also be a logistical issue such as deciding how many students can work on Measuring Ourselves at once or reminding students to return their Inventory Bag, with the same number of items as when they started, to the agreed upon location or a management issue, such as sharing materials, working productively, being a good partner.

Other alternatives include checking in with students about which activities they have been choosing (e.g., "Thumbs up if you measured yourself. Thumbs up if you worked on Inventory Bags. Thumbs up if you played *Collect 20 Together*."), asking everyone to hold up a piece of work, or allowing students to raise a question or make a comment about today's math class.

SESSION FOLLOW-UP

4 Practice

Student Math Handbook Flip Chart: Use the *Student Math Handbook Flip Chart* pages 19, 38 to reinforce concepts from today's session. See pages 189–193 in the back of this unit.

Do We Have to Count Them All?

Math Focus Points

- Developing strategies for accurately counting and keeping track of quantities up to 20
- Finding the total after 1, 2, or 3 is added to, or subtracted from, a set
- Repeating multiple nonstandard units to quantify length

Today's Plan		Materials
DISCUSSION **① Do We Have to Count Them All?** 10 MIN CLASS		• Materials from Sessions 2.1, p. 68
MATH WORKSHOP **② Counting and Measuring** **2A Measuring Ourselves** **2B Inventory Bags** **2C *Collect 20 Together*** 15–30 MIN		2A • Materials from Session 2.3, p. 79 2B • Materials from Session 2.2, p. 74 2C • Materials from Session 2.2, p. 74
DISCUSSION **③ Checking In** 5 MIN CLASS		
SESSION FOLLOW-UP **④ Practice**		• *Student Math Handbook Flip Chart,* pp. 12, 13, 19

Classroom Routines

Calendar: Mixed Up Calendar Choose two date cards and change their positions on the calendar so that they are out of order. Challenge students to find the mistakes and help you fix them.

DISCUSSION

Do We Have to Count Them All?

10 MIN CLASS

Math Focus Points for Discussion

◆ Developing strategies for accurately counting and keeping track of quantities up to 20

◆ Finding the total after 1, 2, or 3 is added to, or subtracted from, a set

Begin this session with a discussion about the strategies students are using to figure out the total number of pennies after each round of *Collect 20 Together.*

I'm interested in how you are figuring out how many pennies you have after each roll in *Collect 20.* Let's play a game together so we can talk about those strategies.

Ask two volunteers to take turns rolling the dot cube and counting out that many pennies.

[Jack] rolled a [3] and took [3] pennies. Then [Raul] rolled a [2] and added [2] more pennies. How can we figure out how many pennies we have altogether?

Some students suggest counting all the pennies. Others suggest starting from the number of pennies you had before and counting on. Ask students to model both strategies. Then, ask students about the latter.

I noticed that [Kaitlyn] did something interesting. She used something she knew. She remembered that we had [3] pennies before [gesture over the pile of 3] and said, "We had [3], now we have [2] more, so [4], [5]. There's [5] pennies." She didn't even count these [3] pennies. Can she do that? Doesn't she need to count all of the pennies?

Some students may be counting on or may begin to experiment with it. Expect others to continue to count all each time they need to find the total.

Continue with the sample game, asking different students to figure out how many pennies there are after each roll. As the number of pennies grows, use this as an opportunity to review and practice the names and sequence of numbers in the teens.❶

MATH WORKSHOP

Counting and Measuring

15–30 MIN

Explain that three activities are available during Math Workshop. Remind students what each activity entails, what materials are required, and where they are located.

All students need to have finished their inventory of the first bag you specified by the end of this Math Workshop, in preparation for the discussion at the beginning of Session 2.5.

2A Measuring Ourselves
PAIRS

For complete details on this activity, see Sessions 2.3, page 80.

2B Inventory Bags
PAIRS

For complete details on this activity, see Session 2.2, page 75.

Also, watch for any students who are using or experimenting with counting on, or combining small groups and then counting on, after the discussion at the beginning of this session.

2C Collect 20 Together
PAIRS

For complete details on this activity, see Session 2.2, page 77.

ONGOING ASSESSMENT: Observing Students at Work

After the discussion at the beginning of this session, watch for any students who are using or experimenting with counting on.

DISCUSSION

Checking In

5 MIN CLASS

Take this opportunity to discuss any issues that you noticed while observing students at work. The topic might be mathematical in nature, such as a strategy you would like all students to consider (e.g., strategies for representing inventories) or a common error or misconception you would like students to discuss (e.g., skipping or double counting objects, or omitting or repeating numbers while counting).

It could also be a logistical issue (e.g., keeping track of which Inventory Bags they have inventoried or keeping the contents of Inventory Bags intact) or a management issue (e.g., sharing materials, working productively, being a helpful partner).

Other alternatives include checking in with students about which activities they have been choosing (e.g., "Thumbs up if you measured yourself. Thumbs up if you worked on Inventory Bags. Thumbs up if you played *Collect 20 Together*."), asking everyone to hold up a piece of work, or allowing students to raise a question or make a comment about today's math class.

SESSION FOLLOW-UP
Practice

Student Math Handbook Flip Chart: Use the *Student Math Handbook Flip Chart* pages 12, 13, 19 to reinforce concepts from today's session. See pages 189–193 in the back of this unit.

How Did You Count?

Math Focus Points

◆ Using subsets to count a set of objects

◆ Repeating multiple nonstandard units to quantify length

◆ Developing strategies for accurately counting and keeping track of quantities up to 20

Today's Plan		Materials
DISCUSSION ① **How Did You Count?** 🕐 10 MIN 👥 CLASS		
MATH WORKSHOP ② **Counting and Measuring** ②A Measuring Ourselves ②B Inventory Bags ②C Collect 20 Together 🕐 15–30 MIN		②A • Materials from Session 2.3, p. 79 ②B • Materials from Session 2.2, p. 74 ②C • Materials from Session 2.2, p. 74
DISCUSSION ③ **Checking In** 🕐 5 MIN 👥 CLASS		
SESSION FOLLOW-UP ④ **Practice**		• *Student Math Handbook Flip Chart,* pp. 19, 38

Classroom Routines

Patterns on the Pocket Chart: Wraparound Patterns Arrange an ABCD repeating pattern on the first two rows of the pocket chart using 14 or more square tiles (red, yellow, green, blue). Cover the eighth through the last square tile with Question Mark Cards. Follow the basic *Patterns* activity. Students hold up the square tile that they think is under each Question Mark Card.

DISCUSSION

How Did You Count?

10 MIN   CLASS

Math Focus Points For Discussion

◆ Using subsets to count a set of objects

Begin this session with a conversation about the first bag inventoried by students. Have students refer to their sheets for the first required Inventory Bag. Focus the discussion on strategies for counting larger quantities and for combining small amounts.

Everyone has taken an inventory of the items in Bag [B]. Here's what was in Bag [B]. How did you find out how many of each item there were? How many items altogether? What did you do first?

Ask a student who began by sorting the items into like groups to do so.

[Mitchell] said he put the [yellows] together, the [reds] together, the [greens] together, and the [blues] together. [Mitchell], will you show us what you mean? Who else put the tiles into groups by color to count them?

Next, ask volunteers to count the number of [tiles] in each group, and ask students to check their papers to see whether everyone agrees on the number in each group. Discuss any discrepancies, and consider why they happen and whether they matter.

Finally, ask students how they figured out how many items were in the bag altogether. Model the different strategies students suggest, which are likely to include counting them all from one, combining the number in small subsets, and then counting the rest. Ask students to consult their paper again to see whether there is agreement on the total number of items in the bag, discuss any discrepancies, and consider why they happen and whether they matter.

MATH WORKSHOP

② Counting and Measuring

15–30 MIN

Explain that three activities are available during Math Workshop. Remind students what each activity entails, what materials are required, and where they are located.

②A Measuring Ourselves

PAIRS

For complete details on this activity, see Session 2.3, page 80.

②B Inventory Bags

PAIRS

For complete details on this activity, see Session 2.2, page 75.

Watch for any students who are using or experimenting with counting on, which was discussed at the beginning of Session 2.4.

②C *Collect 20 Together*

PAIRS

For complete details on this activity, see Session 2.2, page 77.

Again watch for any students who are using or experimenting with counting on, which was discussed at the beginning of Session 2.4.

DISCUSSION

③ Checking In

5 MIN   CLASS

Take this opportunity to discuss any issues you noticed while observing students at work. The topic might be mathematical in nature, such as a strategy you would like all students to consider (e.g., one partner touching each cube while the other keeps track of the numbers on the number line, using addition notation to record an inventory) or a common error or misconception you would like students to discuss (e.g., reversals in the teen numbers, for example writing 21 instead of 12).

Teaching Note

 Preparing for Session 2.6 Collect the recording sheets for the second Inventory Bag that you asked all students to inventory. Sort through them, noticing the different ways students recorded their work. Choose a representative sample to display during the discussion in Session 2.6.

It could also be a logistical issue (e.g., keeping track of which Inventory Bags they have inventoried, keeping the contents of Inventory Bags intact) or a management issue (e.g., sharing materials, working productively, being a helpful partner).

Other alternatives include checking in with students about which activities they have been choosing (e.g., "Thumbs up if you measured yourself. Thumbs up if you worked on Inventory Bags. Thumbs up if you played *Collect 20 Together*."), asking everyone to hold up a piece of work, or allowing students to raise a question or make a comment about today's math class.

SESSION FOLLOW-UP

Practice

Student Math Handbook Flip Chart: Use the *Student Math Handbook Flip Chart* pages 19, 38 to reinforce concepts from today's session. See pages 189–193 in the back of this unit.

Representing an Inventory

Math Focus Points

◆ Developing strategies for accurately counting and keeping track of quantities up to 20

◆ Repeating multiple nonstandard units to quantify length

◆ Using numbers, pictures, and/or words to represent a quantity or measurement

Today's Plan		Materials
① ACTIVITY **Introducing the Counting Jar** 5 MIN CLASS		• Counting Jar*
② MATH WORKSHOP **More Counting and Measuring** **2A** Counting Jar **2B** Measuring Ourselves **2C** Inventory Bags **2D** *Collect 20 Together* 15–30 MIN		**2A** • M12* ☑ • Materials from Activity 1; materials for the Counting Jar routine (as you have set it up) **2B** • Materials from Session 2.3, p. 79 **2C** • Materials from Session 2.2, p. 74 **2D** • Materials from Session 2.2, p. 74
③ DISCUSSION **Representing an Inventory** 10 MIN CLASS		• Work samples*
④ SESSION FOLLOW-UP **Practice**		• *Student Activity Book*, p. 58

*See *Materials to Prepare,* p. 67.

Classroom Routines

Attendance: Counting Forward and Backward Count around the circle as usual. Then have students count backward from the total number to one. Begin with the student who counted last so that each student will say the same number but the count will be backward rather than forward. Encourage students to use the calendar or the number line to help them keep track of the numbers.

Teaching Notes

❶ Assembling a Portfolio Because students do Counting Jar in every unit it provides an opportunity to see students' growth over time. Therefore, have students record their work for one of the two Counting Jars in this unit on a piece of paper you can collect and put in their portfolio. If you did not do this for the Counting Jar in Investigation 1, this is your last opportunity in this unit.

❷ Assessing Addition By the end of this unit, students are expected to be able to combine small amounts accurately (Benchmark 3). This means that they can visualize and model the action of a problem and can use manipulatives—their fingers, drawings, or another strategy—to count all, count on, or add to find the total. Use this activity to see whether any students see this Counting Jar as an addition situation and to plan for Investigation 3, which focuses on addition. You can jot notes on Assessment Checklist: Addition (M12).

Professional Development

❸ Teacher Note: Assessing Addition p. 168

ACTIVITY
① Introducing the Counting Jar

5 MIN   CLASS

Place five red and five blue square tiles in the Counting Jar and show it to students.

I've put a new set of objects in the Counting Jar. Your job is to visit the jar at some point over the next few days and find out how many things are in it. Then, you make a set that has the same number of items and record what you found out.

MATH WORKSHOP
② More Counting and Measuring

15–30 MIN

Explain that four activities are available during Math Workshop and this is the last day that Measuring Ourselves, Inventory Bags, and *Collect 20 Together* will be available. Remind students what each activity entails, what materials are required, and where they are located.

Ask any students who have not taken inventory of the second bag you specified to begin with that activity. They should bring you their completed sheet for that bag when they are done. (If any of these represent a different method of recording, add it to the set you will display during the discussion at the end of this session.)

. . . .

②A Counting Jar

INDIVIDUALS

Students count the objects in the Counting Jar—five red and five blue tiles. They make a set of the same size and then find a way to record what they found out.❶

ONGOING ASSESSMENT: Observing Students at Work

Students count a set of objects, create an equivalent set, and record their work.❷

- **How do students count the objects in the jar?** Do they use the subsets? For example, do they put the tiles in two groups, by color? Do they count them from one? Count on from 5 to find the total? Just know that 5 and 5 is 10?❸

- **How do students record their work?** Do they use numbers, pictures, notation, or a combination? Do any students show the subsets in their work?

- **How do students create an equivalent set?** Do any make a set with 5 of one kind and 5 of another? Do students use Assessment Checklist: Addition (M12) properly?

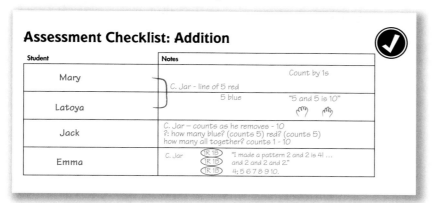

Assessment Checklist: Addition

Student	Notes		
Mary			Count by 1s
	C. Jar - line of 5 red		
Latoya	5 blue		"5 and 5 is 10"
Jack	C. Jar – counts as he removes - 10 ?: how many blue? (counts 5) red? (counts 5) how many all together? counts 1 - 10		
Emma	C. Jar	TR 1B / TR 1B / TR 1B	"I made a pattern 2 and 2 is 4! ... and 2 and 2 and 2." 4; 5 6 7 8 9 10.

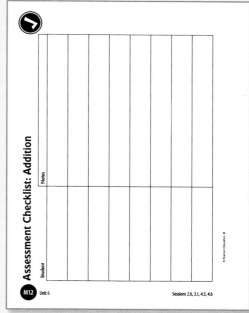

Assessment Checklist: Addition

Student	Notes					

M12 Unit 6   Sessions 2.6, 3.1, 4.5, 4.6

▲ **Resource Masters, M12** ✓

2B Measuring Ourselves
PAIRS

For complete details on this activity, see Session 2.3, page 80.

2C Inventory Bags
PAIRS

For complete details on this activity, see Session 2.2, pages 75–76.

2D *Collect 20 Together*
PAIRS

For complete details on this activity, see Session 2.2, page 77.

DISCUSSION
10 MIN   CLASS

3 Representing an Inventory

Math Focus Points for Discussion

◆ Using numbers, pictures, and/or words to represent a quantity

End this session with a conversation about the second of the Inventory Bags you asked all students to inventory. Post a sample (or all) of the recording sheets for that bag and focus the discussion on strategies for recording.

This week, every pair took an inventory of the items in Bag [C]. Here are some of your recording sheets for that bag. Take a minute to look them over. What do you notice? What do these recording sheets tell us about Bag [C]?

Name _____ Date _____
How Many Do You Have?   Practice

Inventory Bags

Count the number of crayons, markers, and pencils.

Count how many there are in all.

_____ pencils ◄━━━━━━━

_____ crayons ◄━━━━━

_____ markers ◄━━━━

How many are there in all? _____

58 Unit 6   Session 2.6

▲ **Student Activity Book, p. 58**

As students share, ask them to point out the piece(s) of work that show what they noticed.

[Dennis] says he can tell that there were [17] things in Bag [C]. Which paper(s) do you think [Dennis] was looking at? Interesting, we see a [17] on [Mia]'s paper and on [Hugo's] paper, and over here, on [Jae's] paper, too. [Dennis], which paper(s) were you looking at?

As you talk about what the recording sheets tell you about the contents of Bag [C], encourage students to consider and compare different methods for recording.

For example, ask:

• What's the same about these recording sheets? What's different?

• Who used pictures? Words? Numbers? Addition notation? Who used a combination of these strategies?

• Which papers show the total number really clearly? The total in each group? The kind(s) of thing(s) that were in the bag?

Over the course of this conversation, be sure to discuss what was in the bag, how many of each kind of thing was in the bag, and the total number of items in the bag. Ask students to consider whether everyone got the same totals, and use the actual Inventory Bag to resolve any disagreements, as needed. Discuss any discrepancies, asking students to consider why they happen and whether they matter.

SESSION FOLLOW-UP

 Practice

Practice: For reinforcement of this unit's content, have students complete *Student Activity Book* page 58.

Mathematical Emphases

Whole Number Operations Making sense of and developing strategies to solve addition and subtraction problems with small numbers

Math Focus Points

◆ Combining two single-digit numbers, with totals to 20

◆ Modeling the action of combining and separating situations

◆ Separating one amount from another

◆ Finding the total after 1, 2, or 3 is added to, or subtracted from, a set

◆ Developing strategies for solving addition and subtraction story problems

Whole Number Operations Using manipulatives, drawings, tools, and notation to show strategies and solutions

Math Focus Points

◆ Using numbers to record how many

◆ Using numbers and/or addition notation to record how many and to represent an addition situation

This Investigation also focuses on

◆ Counting and comparing two quantities to 20 to determine which is more

How Many in All?

	Student Activity Book	Student Math Handbook Flip Chart	Professional Development: Read Ahead of Time	
SESSION 3.1　　　　p. 100				
Roll and Record 3 Students learn a new variation of *Roll and Record* in which they roll two 0-to-5 dot cubes and record the total. Class ends with students acting out story problems about combining and separating, and discussing ways to solve them.	59, 60		• **Algebra Connections in This Unit,** p. 18 • **Teacher Notes:** Assessing Addition, p. 168; Creating Your Own Story Problems, p. 170; Story Problems in Kindergarten, p. 172; Three Approaches to Story Problems in Kindergarten, p. 174 • **Dialogue Box:** How Are These Stories Different?, p. 186	
SESSION 3.2　　　　p. 105				
Double Compare Students revisit *Double Compare*, a card game in which players turn over two cards and then compare their totals to see which is larger. Math Workshop focuses on counting, combining, and comparing, and class discussion focuses on strategies for playing *Double Compare*.		11, 12, 21	• **Teacher Note:** *Double Compare:* Strategies for Combining and Comparing, p. 176 • **Dialogue Box:** Both of My Numbers Were Bigger, p. 187	
SESSION 3.3　　　　p. 110				
Modeling Story Problems Students use cubes to model the action of combining and separating situations. Math Workshop focuses on counting, combining, and comparing. Class discussion focuses on the two sets of five tiles in the Counting Jar.	61			
SESSION 3.4　　　　p. 115				
Build and Remove Students play *Build and Remove*, a game that involves building an amount on a Ten-Frame, removing some, and determining what is left. Math Workshop focuses on combining, comparing, and subtracting small amounts.	62	26, 31, 32		

Classroom Routines See page 20 for an overview.

Today's Question	*Calendar*
• *Today's Question* charts for Sessions 3.1 and 3.5. See instructions on pages 100 and 119.	• Class calendar or class pocket calendar
Patterns on the Pocket Chart	*Attendance*
• Pocket Chart(s) or Sentence Pocket Chart	• No materials needed
• M7, Question Mark Cards (from Investigation 1)	
• M14, Arrow Cards, cut apart.	
• Cups or bags of square tiles	

Materials to Gather	Materials to Prepare
• **Materials for Counting Jar** See Session 2.6.	• **M13, *Roll and Record 3* Recording Sheet** Make copies. (1 per student) • **0-to-5 dot cubes** Cover the 6 on a 1-to-6 dot cube with a blank stick-on dot. (2 per student)
• **Cubes or other counters** (25 per pair) • **0-to-5 number cube** (as needed) • **Materials for *Roll and Record 3*** See Session 3.1. • **Materials for Counting Jar** See Session 2.6.	• **M15–M18, Primary Number Cards** If you are not using the manufactured decks, make copies on cardstock and laminate. Cut apart. (1 deck per pair with Wild Cards removed)
• **Pencils** (7 per class) • **Cubes** (10 per pair) • **Materials for *Double Compare*** See Session 3.2. • **Materials for *Roll and Record 3*** See Session 3.1. • **Materials for Counting Jar** See Session 2.6.	
• **1-to-3 dot cubes** (1 per pair; from Investigation 2) • **Counters** (10 per pair) • **Primary Number Cards** (0–3 and Wild Cards removed from each deck) • **Materials for *Double Compare*** See Session 3.2. • **Materials for *Roll and Record 3*** See Session 3.1. • **Shells** • **Cubes** (10 per pair)	• **M11, Ten-Frame** Make copies. (as needed) • **M21, *Build and Remove*** Make copies. (extra copies as needed)

☑ Checklist Available

How Many in All?, *continued*

	Student Activity Book	Student Math Handbook Flip Chart	Professional Development: Read Ahead of Time	
SESSION 3.5 p. 119				
How Many Balls? Students solve a story problem and record their work on paper. Math Workshop continues to focus on combining, comparing, and subtracting small amounts. Class discussion focuses on different ways students recorded their solution to the story problem.	63	26, 31, 32		
SESSION 3.6 p. 123				
How Do You Show the One That Is Gone? Students solve another story problem and record their work on paper. Math Workshop continues to focus on combining, comparing, and subtracting small amounts. Class discussion focuses on different ways students recorded their solution to the story problem.	64	31, 32, 33, 34		
SESSION 3.7 p. 128				
How Many Blocks? Students solve a story problem and record their work on paper. Math Workshop continues to focus on combining, comparing, and subtracting small amounts. Class discussion focuses on different ways students recorded their solution to the story problem.	65	31, 32, 33, 34		

Materials to Gather	Materials to Prepare
• **Cubes or other counters** • **Materials for** *Build and Remove* See Session 3.4. • **Materials for** *Double Compare* See Session 3.2. • **Materials for** *Roll and Record 3* See Session 3.1.	• **M19–M20, Family Letter** Make copies. (1 per student)
• **Cubes or other counters** • **Materials for** *Build and Remove* See Session 3.4. • **Materials for** *Double Compare* See Session 3.2. • **Materials for** *Roll and Record 3* See Session 3.1.	
• **Cubes or other counters** • **Materials for** *Build and Remove* See Session 3.4. • **Materials for** *Double Compare* See Session 3.2. • **Materials for** *Roll and Record 3* See Session 3.1.	

Roll and Record 3

Math Focus Points

- Combining two single-digit numbers, with totals to 10
- Using numbers to record how many
- Modeling the action of combining and separating situations
- Separating one amount from another

Today's Plan			Materials
ACTIVITY **① Introducing *Roll and Record 3***	5 MIN	CLASS	• M13* • 0-to-5 dot cubes*
MATH WORKSHOP **② Counting and Combining** **②A** *Roll and Record 3* **②B** Counting Jar	15–30 MIN		**②A** • *Student Activity Book,* p. 59 • M13* • Counters; 0-to-5 dot cubes* **②B** • Materials from Session 2.6, p. 91
ACTIVITY **③ Acting Out Story Problems**	10 MIN	CLASS	
SESSION FOLLOW-UP **④ Practice**			• *Student Activity Book,* p. 60

*See *Materials to Prepare,* p. 97.

Classroom Routines

Today's Question: Do you have the letter M in your name? **On chart paper, create a vertical two-column table with rows drawn in, titled "Do you have the letter M in your name?" with "Yes" written at the bottom of one column and "No" written at the bottom of the other column. Students respond by writing their names in the appropriate column. As you discuss the result of the survey, ask students how the new table helps them count and compare the data.**

ACTIVITY

Introducing *Roll and Record 3*

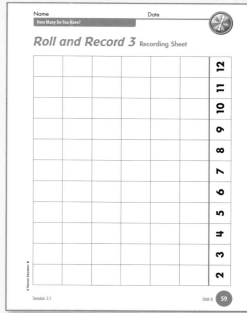

▲ Student Activity Book, p. 59; Resource Masters, M13

5 MIN   CLASS

In *Counting and Comparing*, students played *Roll and Record* with a 1-to-6 dot cube. In *Measuring and Counting*, students used a 1-to-6 and 1-to-3 dot cube. Ask students what they recall about these earlier versions, and introduce the new variation.

Today we are going to play another variation of *Roll and Record*. We are going to use two dot cubes.

Show students the 0-to-5 dot cubes and ask what they notice. Be sure to discuss how each cube has dots that show the numbers 1-to-5 and one blank side, for 0.

When you play *Roll and Record* you are going to roll two 0-to-5 dot cubes. Let's try it. What did I roll? How many dots do you see altogether? How did you figure that out? Did anyone figure it out a different way?

Expect many students to count all of the dots from one. Others use their fingers, count on, or "just know" some of the combinations at this point in the year. A few may even use a combination they know $(4 + 4)$ to figure out one that they do not know $(4 + 5)$.

So we agree that there were [nine] dots. Where should I write [9] on my recording sheet? What if I didn't know how to write the number [9]? Where in our classroom could I look?

Use the tools students suggest, which may include the number line, calendar, or *Roll and Record 3: Recording Sheet* (M13) to figure out how to write a 9, and then model writing it in the correct column.

Ask one or several volunteers to roll the dot cubes a few more times, modeling ways to find and record the total. Remind students that the game is finished when one of the columns is completely filled.

MATH WORKSHOP

Counting and Combining

15–30 MIN

Explain that two activities are available during Math Workshop. Remind students what each activity entails, what materials are required, and where they are located.

Teaching Notes

❶ Assembling a Portfolio Students played variations of *Roll and Record* in *Counting and Comparing* and *Measuring and Counting*. Placing a recording sheet from each, as well as one from *Roll and Record 3* in their portfolio will provide a picture of students' growth in writing the numbers over the course of the year.

❷ Assessing Students' Written Numbers *Roll and Record 3* offers a particularly efficient way to assess students' writing of the numbers to 10 (Benchmark 1). Continue using Assessment Checklist: Writing Numbers to 10 (M5) to keep track of your observations.

❸ Assessing Addition The bulk of Investigation 3 focuses on addition. Continue to use Assessment Checklist: Addition (M12) to keep track of your observations about students' strategies for combining two small amounts (Benchmark 3).

Professional Development

❹ Teacher Note: Assessing Addition, p. 168

---

②A *Roll and Record 3*

INDIVIDUALS

Students roll two 0-to-5 dot cubes, find the total, and record that number on *Student Activity Book* page 59. Students can play alone or in pairs, but each needs to record on his or her own recording sheet.❶

ONGOING ASSESSMENT: Observing Students at Work

Students count and combine small amounts and practice writing the numerals to 10.❷ ❸ ❹

- **How do students determine the total number of dots?** Do they count them all, count on, or use a number combination they "just know"?

- **How do students figure out what number to write and where to write it?** Do they "just know"? Do they count up on a number line? Can they write the numbers accurately and legibly? Which numbers are most problematic?

Assessment Checklist: Writing Numbers to 10 ✓

Student	1	2	3	4	5	6	7	8	9	10	Notes (Ⓟ = reversal)
Shavonne	✓	✓	Ⓟ/Ⓟ	Ⓟ/✓	✓	Ⓟ/Ⓟ	—/Ⓟ	✓	—/Ⓟ	✓	Toss the Chips / R+R
Dennis	✓	✓	Ⓟ/✓	✓	Ⓟ/Ⓟ	✓	✓	✓	✓	✓	Tiles / R+R
Mitchell	✓	Ⓟ/✓	Ⓟ/Ⓟ	✓	✓	Ⓟ/Ⓟ	✓	✓	Ⓟ/✓	✓	Tiles / R+R
Kaitlyn	✓	✓	✓	✓	✓	✓	✓	✓	✓	✓/✓	Chips / R+R
Kyle	✓	✓	✓	✓	✓	✓	Ⓟ/Ⓟ	✓	✓	✓	Tiles / R+R
Jennifer	✓	✓	✓	✓	✓	✓	✓	✓	✓	✓	Roll & Record
Mary	✓	Ⓟ	✓	✓	✓	✓	✓	✓	✓		
Kiyo	✓	✓	✓	Ⓟ	✓	Ⓟ	✓	✓	✓	✓	
Timothy	✓	✓	✓	✓	✓	✓	✓	✓	✓	✓	
Raul	✓	✓	✓	✓	✓	✓	✓	✓	✓		
Abby	✓	✓	Ⓟ	✓	✓	✓	✓	✓	✓	✓	

DIFFERENTIATION: Supporting the Range of Learners

Intervention Because the dot cubes are small, some students may count more accurately if they use counters to recreate the dot images. If students are having difficulty accurately *forming* the numbers, make this a focus of your handwriting curriculum.

Extension Students often become very interested in which number "wins." Although the goal of this game is connecting numbers and quantities, you can ask these students questions about their completed game page.

Which number did you roll the *least?* . . . How many times did you roll a 1?

2B Counting Jar

INDIVIDUALS

For complete details on this activity, see Session 2.6, page 92.

ACTIVITY

3 Acting Out Story Problems

10 MIN **CLASS**

Remind students of the work they did visualizing, retelling, and acting out story problems in *Measuring and Counting.* Explain that, just as you did in that unit, you are going to tell a story and that, while students are listening, they should try to see the story in their minds. Some may want to close their eyes to help them concentrate. Draw quick sketches of important words on the board to support students who are not English-proficient.⑤ ⑥

Four children were at the playground, playing on the swings. Then one of the children went home for dinner. Who can tell me what happened?

Follow the same process as in *Measuring and Counting:* ask several students to retell the story in their own words, have volunteers act out the story, and then discuss strategies for figuring out how many children were still on the swings at the end of the story.⑦ ⑧ These strategies are likely to include counting the student actors who remain at the swings, counting on their fingers, counting back 1 from 4, or "just knowing" that 3 is 1 less than 4.⑨

Next, tell a related story that involves combining two amounts, but do not mention that the story will be different in any way. The goal is for students to think about the action in the story and choose a strategy that reflects that action.

So now there were three children playing on the swings. Then [Abby] and her little brother came to play at the park. They joined the children who were playing on the swings.

Again, have several students retell the story, ask volunteers to act it out, and gather strategies for figuring out how many children are playing on the swings now. These strategies are likely to include counting all of the student actors, counting on their fingers, counting on from 3, or "just knowing" that 3 and 2 is 5.⑨

Teaching Note

⑤ **Choosing Appropriate Problems** It is important to choose problems that your students can easily visualize and act out. If the context of a story is unfamiliar, choose another but keep the numbers the same.

Math Note

⑦ **Story Problems** Retelling and acting out stories help students think about, visualize, and make sense of the action in a problem—a crucial step in solving an addition or subtraction story problem.

Professional Development

⑥ **Teacher Note:** Creating Your Own Story Problems, p. 170

⑧ **Teacher Note:** Story Problems in Kindergarten, p. 172

⑨ **Teacher Note:** Three Approaches to Story Problems in Kindergarten, p. 174

Algebra Note

⑩ **Comparing Stories** By discussing how two stories are different, students begin to develop a sense of how the operations of addition and subtraction behave. See Algebra Connections in This Unit, p. 18.

Professional Development

⑪ **Dialogue Box:** How Are These Stories Different?, p. 186

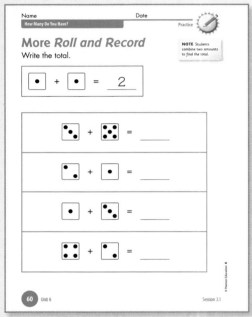

▲ Student Activity Book, p. 60

If no one comments on how these two stories are similar or different, raise these questions yourself.

How were these two stories similar? What was the same about them? How were they different?

When students think about how these problems are similar, they talk about the characters (children, actors), the context (the playground, the swing set), and possibly the fact that both stories involved a group of three children.

A discussion of the difference between these two stories should focus on the action: in the second story, two groups came together, but in the first, one went away. Or, in the second story there were more children at the end, and in the first story, there were fewer.⑩ ⑪

As time permits, tell another story or two. For example:

[Hugo] had 4 flowers. He gave 2 flowers to his mom. How many flowers does [Hugo] have now?

[Tammy] has 6 toy cars. [Mitchell] gave her 2 more cars. How many toy cars does she have now?

After students share strategies for solving a problem, ask the following:

Was this story about putting groups together or about taking away part of a group? How do you know? [Sarah] thinks it's about taking away part of a group because Hugo gave away some flowers. Does anyone have another idea?

As students become more familiar with this activity, you can add to the level of challenge with a new kind of question.

Everyone says that this story is about putting groups together, because [Tammy] had her six toy cars *and* the group of two that [Mitchell] gave her. Who has an idea for a story about toy cars in which part of a group is taken away?

SESSION FOLLOW-UP

4 Practice

 Practice: For reinforcement of this unit's content, have students complete *Student Activity Book* page 60.

Double Compare

Math Focus Points

◆ Combining two single-digit numbers, with totals to 12

◆ Using numbers to record how many

◆ Counting and comparing quantities to 12 to determine which is more

Vocabulary

more

Today's Plan		Materials
ACTIVITY **①** Introducing *Double Compare*	5 MIN / CLASS	• M15–M18* • Cubes or other counters
MATH WORKSHOP **②** Counting, Combining, and Comparing **2A** *Double Compare* **2B** *Roll and Record 3* **2C** *Counting Jar*	15–30 MIN	**2A** • Materials from Activity 1 **2B** • Materials from Session 3.1, p. 100 • 0-to-5 number cubes **2C** • Materials from Session 2.6, p. 91
DISCUSSION **③** *Double Compare*	10 MIN / CLASS	• Materials from Activity 1
SESSION FOLLOW-UP **④** Practice		• *Student Math Handbook Flip Chart,* pp. 11, 12, 21

*See *Materials to Prepare*, p. 97.

Classroom Routines

Patterns on the Pocket Chart: Wraparound Patterns Arrange an ABB repeating pattern on the first two rows of the pocket chart using 14 or more Arrow Cards (M14) (up, left, left). Cover the eighth through the last Arrow Card with Question Mark Cards. Follow the basic *Patterns* activity. Students point in the direction that they think is under each Question Mark Card.

Teaching Note

❶ Being a Helpful Partner If students are playing too competitively, emphasize that getting the larger total is a matter of luck, not of being a better player. Explain that good players check or help each other, explain their thinking, ask each other for help, and wait patiently while a partner finds a total or determines which number is larger.

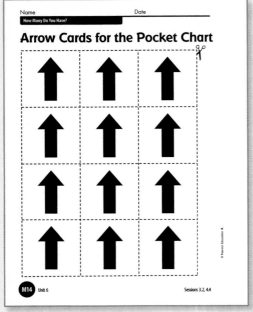

Name _____ Date _____
How Many Do You Have?

Arrow Cards for the Pocket Chart

M14 Unit 6   Sessions 3.2, 4.4

▲ Resource Masters, M14

5 MIN   CLASS

ACTIVITY
Introducing *Double Compare*

This game should need only a brief introduction, as students played it in *Measuring and Counting*.

In this game each player turns over two Primary Number Cards (M15–M18). Then you compare the total of your cards to the total of your partner's cards. The player with the larger total says "Me."

Enlist volunteers to play a demonstration game, or choose a student to play with you. Have counters available for figuring out or comparing totals.

[Shavonne] turned over [5] and [1]. [Brad] turned over [5] and [4]. Who has **more**? How do you know? Did anyone think about it in a different way?

Ask students to explain how they decided which player had the larger total. Expect a range of strategies.

Remind students that any time players have the same total, they turn over the next two cards and compare those totals and that the game is over when players have turned over all their cards.

15–30 MIN

MATH WORKSHOP
Counting, Combining, and Comparing

Explain that three activities are available during Math Workshop. Remind students what each activity entails, what materials are required, and where they are located.

2A *Double Compare*

PAIRS

Each player turns over two Primary Number Cards. Then players decide which pair of cards shows the larger total.❶

ONGOING ASSESSMENT: Observing Students at Work

Students combine and compare numbers with totals up to 12.

- **Do students recognize the numbers on the cards?** Or, do they count the pictures to determine the number? Can they count them accurately?

- **Do students combine the two quantities?** How? Do they count all or count up from one of the numbers? Do they use counters or pictures on the cards? Do they "just know" any of the sums? Which ones?

- **How do students determine which total is larger?** Do they build and compare cube towers? Do they compare the numbers on the number line? Do they "just know" which number is bigger?

- **Do any students reason about which total is larger without actually finding the total?** For example, "I got 3 and 4, and you got 3 and 2. I have more because the threes are the same and 4 is bigger than 2."

As you observe students at work, pay particular attention to the strategies they use to inform the discussion at the end of this session.❷

DIFFERENTIATION: Supporting the Range of Learners

Intervention For some students, counting the pictures on the cards is challenging. Encourage them to use cubes or counters to create sets that match the cards. Then they can count the cubes to find the total. Similarly, students who are having difficulty comparing quantities can build and compare cube towers.

Extension If students are able to determine who says "Me" without counting the totals, ask them to explain their thinking. Ask what is special about their cards that allows them to do that, and whether they think that strategy would work with other numbers.❸

. . . .

②B *Roll and Record 3*

INDIVIDUALS

For complete details on this activity, see Session 3.1, pages 101–102.

Professional Development

❷ **Teacher Note:** *Double Compare:* Strategies for Combining and Comparing, p. 176

Algebra Note

❸ **Comparing Without Combining** If students can determine who has more without combining, they may be acting on a generalization—a general claim you can make about the way numbers or operations work. For example, they might be using the idea that if both players have one card that is the same, then they can compare the other two cards to see who has the larger total.

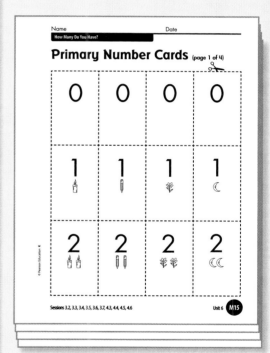

▲ Resource Masters, M15–M18

---

❹ **Dialogue Box:** Both of My Numbers Were Bigger,
p. 187

DIFFERENTIATION: Supporting the Range of Learners

Extension Students who are counting on or using combinations they know to figure out their total might be ready to play with a 0-to-5 number cube and a 0-to-5 dot cube.

2C Counting Jar

INDIVIDUALS

For complete details on this activity, see Session 2.6, page 92.

DISCUSSION

10 MIN CLASS

3 Double Compare

Math Focus Points for Discussion

◆ Counting and comparing quantities to 12 to determine which is more

Call students together for a discussion about the strategies they are using as they play *Double Compare*.❹ Turn over four Primary Number Cards to create a problem. Ask everyone to think quietly about which hand has more and how they know. Have cubes or other counters available for students to use to combine or compare.

I got a [1] and a [2], and [Brad] got a [5] and a [3]. Think quietly for a minute. Who has more? How do you know?

Many students combine the amounts on the cards and then compare the totals. Most count all, some count on, and others just know the combinations. Have volunteers share and model these strategies.

Then, focus on the strategies of students who did *not* find the total as they played. For example, for this problem:

Students might say:

"Both of [Brad's] numbers are bigger, so he has more."

"Brad got two bigger numbers and you got two small numbers, so he has more."

 "You have 2 and 1 and that's 3 altogether. Brad's already got 3 and he has a 5, so he has more."

From what you have observed of students at work, present problems that involve specific numbers in order to provide the opportunity to discuss a particular strategy. For example, many students discover that they do not need to count when both players get one card that is the same.

Okay, let's play another round. I got [6] and [2]. [Kiyo] got [6] and [5]. Who has more? How do you know?

Students might say:

 "These [pointing to the 6s] are the same. Then 2's small. So Kiyo has more because 5's big."

 "You both have 6. Kiyo has more because 5 is more than 2."

 "You had 6 and Kiyo had 6. And then Kiyo had a higher number."

SESSION FOLLOW-UP
Practice

 Student Math Handbook Flip Chart: Use the *Student Math Handbook Flip Chart* pages 11, 12, 21 to reinforce concepts from today's session. See pages 189–193 in the back of this unit.

Modeling Story Problems

Math Focus Points

◆ Modeling the action of combining and separating situations

◆ Counting and comparing quantities to 20 to determine which is more

◆ Separating one amount from another

◆ Combining two single-digit numbers, with totals to 20

◆ Using numbers and/or addition notation to record how many and to represent an addition situation

Vocabulary

add	combined
plus	equal sign
plus sign	equals

Today's Plan

	Materials
ACTIVITY **①** **Modeling Story Problems** 🕐 10 MIN 👪 CLASS	• Pencils; cubes
MATH WORKSHOP **②** **Counting, Combining, and Comparing** ㉒ *Double Compare* ㉓ *Roll and Record 3* ㉔ Counting Jar 🕐 10–25 MIN	㉒ • Materials from Session 3.2, p. 105 ㉓ • Materials from Session 3.1, p. 100 ㉔ • Materials from Session 2.6, p. 91
DISCUSSION **③** **Counting Jar** 🕐 10 MIN 👪 CLASS	• Materials from Session 2.6, p. 91
SESSION FOLLOW-UP **④** **Practice**	• *Student Activity Book,* p. 61

Classroom Routines

Calendar: How Many Days . . . ? Students use the calendar to determine how many days have passed since a class event or holiday that happened this month. Discuss students' strategies for determining the number of days.

ACTIVITY
① Modeling Story Problems

10 MIN CLASS

Explain that you are going to tell a story and that, while they are listening, students should try to see the story in their minds.

After school yesterday, I was cleaning up over in the block area and I found 3 pencils on the floor. Then I went over to the art table and I found 4 more pencils on the table. Now, who can tell me what happened?

Ask several students to tell what they remember about the story, even if one student tells the story correctly the first time. Encourage students to focus on the actions of the story rather than on what they think the question and answer will be.

Next, choose an actor to act out your story, perhaps using actual pencils. Read the story problem again while the student acts out what happens.

When [Kyle] acted out the story, he took 3 pencils and laid them next to 4 more pencils. I'm wondering whether everyone could use cubes to act out my story.

Give each pair of students more than seven cubes and have them work together to use the cubes to show what happened in the story. Note that using cubes to stand for pencils may be a challenging idea for some students. After students have had time to work, ask a couple of pairs to show how they used the cubes to model your story.

Then, ask students how many pencils you found altogether, keeping the emphasis on solution strategies.

Now tell a related story that involves separating one amount from another, but do not mention that the story will be different in any way.

We just figured out that I found 7 pencils. But when I walked over to put them into the bin, 2 of the pencils fell out of my hand.

This time, give everyone a chance to retell the story:

Take turns telling my story to your partner.

Next, ask students to use cubes to model what happened in the story. After students have put the story in their own words and modeled it with the cubes, ask the following:

How could we tell how many pencils were still in my hand?

Teaching Note

❶ Adding If any students suggest combining the two amounts, ask them to put the story in their own words. You might also invite some students to act out the story again.

Algebra Note

❷ Comparing Stories By discussing how two stories are different, students begin to develop a sense of how the operations of addition and subtraction behave.

Collect solution strategies,❶ and then ask students to compare the two stories.❷

How were the two stories about pencils the same? How were they different?

Be sure to discuss how the actions of the two problems were different. One involved combining or joining two groups, and the other involved removing or separating some from a group. Students often point out the difference between the final quantities: in the first story there were more pencils at the end of the story; in the second there were fewer.

MATH WORKSHOP

10–25 MIN

❷ Counting, Combining, and Comparing

Explain that three activities are available, that *Double Compare* now involves full decks of cards from 0 to 10, and that students need to complete the Counting Jar by the end of this Math Workshop, as you will discuss it at the end of this session. Remind students what each activity entails, what materials are required, and where they are located.

2A *Double Compare*

PAIRS

Students play with all of the cards, from zero to ten, in their decks.

For complete details on this activity, see Session 3.2, page 106.

DIFFERENTIATION: Supporting the Range of Learners

Intervention Some students may benefit from playing in a small group with you, where they can share and see others' strategies for combining and comparing the amounts on the cards. Some may need further practice playing with only the cards to 6.

ELL Addition-related words such as *plus, combine, put together, join,* and *add* may be unfamiliar to some English Language Learners. You can keep a running list of these terms on a piece of chart paper, along with a list of common subtraction-related words such as *minus, subtract,* and *take away.* These lists will support English Language Learners as they work with story problems in the upcoming sessions.

2B Roll and Record 3

INDIVIDUALS

For complete details on this activity, see Session 3.1, pages 101–102.

2C Counting Jar

INDIVIDUALS

For complete details on this activity, see Session 2.6, page 92.

Look over students' completed work for the Counting Jar. Note several different strategies students used to record, to inform the discussion at the end of this Session.

10 MIN   CLASS

DISCUSSION
3 Counting Jar

Math Focus Points for Discussion

◆ Combining two single-digit numbers, with totals to 20

◆ Using numbers and/or addition notation to record how many and to represent an addition situation

Gather students to discuss the Counting Jar. Ask them what they found in the jar and to share anything they noticed about the task this week. Students may comment on there being two different colors of square tiles and on the fact that there were the same number of red as there were blue.

I am curious about how you figured out how many square tiles were in the Counting Jar this week.

Some students count each tile without organizing them in any way. Some students put the tiles in two groups by color, while others put the tiles in groups of two with each group having one red and one blue. These students may count the tiles from one, or use the groups in some way to find the total. Model and discuss each strategy students suggest, but focus in particular on methods that involved seeing the situation as an addition situation.

[Hugo] said there were five blues and five reds, and [Rebecca] said that's 5 plus 5. I'm wondering how people who saw this as a group of five blues and a group of five reds figured out how many tiles there were? How did you add 5 and 5?

▲ **Student Activity Book, p. 61**

Some students count all. Others use the tiles or their fingers to count on from five: "There were five reds and five blues. So 5, 6, 7, 8, 9, 10." Still others may know something about the combination 5 + 5. They may hold up two hands and explain that five fingers on each hand make ten fingers, or be familiar with the doubles combinations and "just know" that 5 + 5 = 10.

You had lots of interesting ways to show that there were ten tiles in the Counting Jar. Some of you also found ways to show that 5 of the tiles were red and 5 of the tiles were blue.

Summarize and model several of the ways that students used to record their work. Then, bring up addition notation.

Before, [Rebecca] said something about 5 plus 5. We talked a little bit about this when we arranged square tiles and did *Quick Images* with square tiles. Does anyone have an idea about how we could use numbers and symbols to show what we found out about this week's Counting Jar?

Work together to write an expression (5 + 5) or even a full equation (5 + 5 = 10), putting words and actions to each number or symbol in the problem, and connecting them to the groups of actual tiles. For example:

[Rebecca] said 5 *plus* 5. I am going to write 5, for the group of blue tiles, and then this **plus sign** and another 5, for the group of red tiles. What does this plus sign mean? . . . Right, it shows that there was one group of five tiles, and we *combined* them with another group of five tiles. The plus sign shows that you *put together* two groups of five, you *joined* them or *added* them together . . . What sign do we use to show that there were ten tiles altogether? . . . Right, the **equal sign**. Five plus 5 **equals** 10. What's on this side (5 + 5) *is the same as* what's on this side (10).

SESSION FOLLOW-UP

4 Practice

Practice: For reinforcement of this unit's content, have students complete *Student Activity Book* page 61.

Build and Remove

Math Focus Points

◆ Finding the total after 1, 2, or 3 is subtracted from a set

◆ Counting and comparing quantities to 20 to determine which is more

◆ Using numbers to record how many

Vocabulary

remove
minus

Today's Plan		Materials
ACTIVITY **①** Introducing *Build and Remove*	⏱ 10 MIN 👥 CLASS	• M11* • M21* • Primary Number Cards (with 0–3 and Wild Cards removed); 1-to-3 dot cube; counters
MATH WORKSHOP **②** Combining, Removing, and Comparing **2A** *Build and Remove* **2B** *Double Compare* **2C** *Roll and Record 3*	⏱ 10–25 MIN	**2A** • *Student Activity Book,* p. 62 • Materials from Activity 1 **2B** • Materials from Session 3.2, p. 105 **2C** • Materials from Session 3.1, p. 100
ACTIVITY **③** Modeling Story Problems	⏱ 10 MIN 👥 CLASS	• Shells; cubes
SESSION FOLLOW-UP **④** Practice		• *Student Math Handbook Flip Chart,* pp. 26, 31, 32

*See *Materials to Prepare,* p. 97.

Classroom Routines

Attendance: Counting Forward and Backward Count around the circle as usual, and then have students count backward from the total number to 1. Begin with the student who counted last so that each student will say the same number but the count will be backward rather than forward. Encourage students to use the calendar or the number line to help them keep track of the numbers.

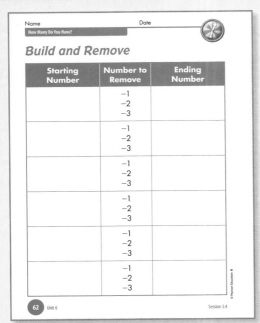

Name _____ Date _____

How Many Do You Have?

Build and Remove

Starting Number	Number to Remove	Ending Number
	−1 −2 −3	
	−1 −2 −3	
	−1 −2 −3	
	−1 −2 −3	
	−1 −2 −3	
	−1 −2 −3	

62 Unit 6   Session 3.4

▲ **Student Activity Book, p. 62;**
Resource Masters, M21

10 MIN   CLASS

ACTIVITY

1 Introducing *Build and Remove*

Explain that students will learn how to play *Build and Remove* today, a game that is similar to *Build On* from *Measuring and Counting*. Have copies of Ten-Frame (M11) available for students to use.

Ask a volunteer to play a few rounds with you to introduce it to the class.

Player 1 turns over the top card, and places that many counters on the Ten-Frame. What number did Victor turn over? (8) How many counters should he place on our Ten-Frame? (8) While Victor puts the counters on the Ten-Frame, I write that number on our Recording Sheet.

Show students where they would record the 8, explaining that when one person is working, it is the other person's job to record.

Now it's my turn. I roll the 1-to-3 dot cube, to see how many counters to remove from the Ten-Frame. What did I roll? (2) So I need to remove two counters.

Model how to record the two counters that were removed on the *Build and Remove* recording sheet (M21).

[Victor] put eight counters on our Ten-Frame and I removed or took away two of them. So, [Victor] circled minus 2. Now our job is to work together to figure out how many counters are left. How could [Victor] and I figure that out?

Some students count the remaining counters from 1. Others use the structure of the Ten-Frame to figure out how many are left: "There's a row of 5 and 1 more. That's 6." A few may see the problem as a subtraction problem and count back from [8] or use their fingers to solve 8 − 2. Model and discuss each strategy that students suggest.

Play another round, changing roles with your partner. Play enough rounds so that students understand how to play.

MATH WORKSHOP

2 Combining, Removing, and Comparing

10–25 MIN

Explain that three activities are available during Math Workshop. Remind students what each activity entails, what materials are required, and where they are located.

2A *Build and Remove*

PAIRS

Player 1 turns over a Primary Number Card and arranges that many counters on a Ten-Frame. Then Player 2 rolls a 1-to-3 dot cube, and removes that many counters from the Ten-Frame. Players work together to figure out how many counters are left and to record their work on *Student Activity Book* page 62.

ONGOING ASSESSMENT: Observing Students at Work

Students read the written numbers, create a set of a given size, and find the total when 1, 2, or 3 is subtracted from that set.

- **How do students figure out the number on the card?** Do they "just know" the name of the number? Do they count the pictures on the card?

- **Are students accurate in their counting?** How do they arrange the counters on the Ten-Frame?

- **How do students find the total after 1, 2, or 3 has been subtracted?** Do they count all? Use the structure of the Ten-Frame? (e.g., "This row has five and one more is six.") Count back from the original total? Pose and solve a subtraction problem? Do any "just know" the answer when one is removed?

DIFFERENTIATION: Supporting the Range of Learners

Intervention Consider playing with a small group of students who are likely to need more support.

....

2B *Double Compare*

PAIRS

For complete details on this activity, see Session 3.2, page 106.

....

2C *Roll and Record 3*

INDIVIDUALS PAIRS

For complete details on this activity, see Session 3.1, pages 101–102.

ACTIVITY
Modeling Story Problems

10 MIN   CLASS

End this session with the whole class solving a story problem. Explain that you are going to tell another story and that while they are listening they should try to see the story in their minds.

[Corey] loves shells. She started a collection of shells that she found at the beach. Her collection had [7] shells in it. [Corey] decided to give [Kaitlyn] one of her favorite shells as a present. Now, who can tell me what happened?

As you did in Session 3.3, ask several students to retell the story in their own words, and then ask pairs to use cubes to act out the story. Discuss how students used the cubes and their strategies for figuring out how many shells [Corey] had at the end of the story.

Repeat this process as time permits. You might tell a related subtraction story:

The next week, [Corey] decided to give another one of her favorite shells to [Kyle]. She wrapped it up and gave it to him. How many shells does [Corey] have now?

You then might tell a related addition story.

The next day [Corey] went back to the beach. She found [2] more shells that she wanted to add to her collection. How many shells does she have now?

SESSION FOLLOW-UP
Practice

Student Math Handbook Flip Chart: Use the *Student Math Handbook Flip Chart* pages 26, 31, 32 to reinforce concepts from today's session. See pages 189–193 in the back of this unit.

How Many Balls?

Math Focus Points

- Modeling the action of combining and separating situations
- Developing strategies for solving addition and subtraction story problems
- Using numbers, pictures, and/or words to represent a solution to a problem

Today's Plan		Materials
① ACTIVITY **Introducing How Many Balls?**	5 MIN CLASS	• *Student Activity Book,* p. 63

② MATH WORKSHOP
Addition and Subtraction:
Story Problems and Games
  2Ⓐ How Many Balls?
  2Ⓑ Build and Remove
  2Ⓒ Double Compare
  2Ⓓ Roll and Record 3
	15–30 MIN	**2A** • *Student Activity Book,* p. 63
		    • Cubes or other counters
		2B • Materials from Session 3.4, p. 115
		2C • Materials from Session 3.2, p. 105
		2D • Materials from Session 3.1, p. 100

③ DISCUSSION **How Did You Record?**	10 MIN CLASS	• Completed copy of *Student Activity Book,* p. 63
④ SESSION FOLLOW-UP **Homework**		• M19–M20, Family Letter

Classroom Routines

Today's Question: Would you rather be a tiger or a dolphin? On chart paper, create a vertical two-column table with rows drawn in, titled "Would you rather be a tiger or a dolphin?" with the heading "Tiger" or "Dolphin" written at the top of each column. Students respond by writing their names in the appropriate column. As you discuss the results of the survey, ask students how the new table helps them count and compare the data.

Teaching Note

Changing the Context Because this activity asks students to record their work on paper, this story uses small numbers and objects that should be fairly easy for kindergarteners to draw. If you change the context of the story, be sure to keep the numbers the same and to use items that are easy to draw, as complicated objects can quickly turn this into an art activity rather than a mathematical one.

▲ Student Activity Book, p. 63

5 MIN   CLASS

ACTIVITY

1 Introducing How Many Balls?

Explain that students will be working on another story problem today, but the process will be a bit different. Tell the following combining story.

[Yoshio] was in charge of cleaning up after recess. He found [three] balls by the swings. Then he found [two] more by the slide.

As usual, ask several students to retell the story in their own words, even if one student tells the story correctly the first time. Encourage students to focus on the actions of the story rather than on what they think the question and answer will be.

Usually the next thing that happens is I ask a question about the story and then we act it out with students or with cubes. Today I'm going to ask the question, and then I'd like you to solve it and find a way to show your solution on paper.

Show them a copy of *Student Activity Book* page 63, read it aloud, and explain the strategies and materials available to them.

So the question you'll be thinking about is how many balls did [Yoshio] find? Remember he found [three] balls by the swings and [two] more by the slide. You can use any of the strategies we've been using to solve it—you can act it out, talk with a partner, or model it with cubes or counters. Drawing a picture might help, too.

Today's challenge, after you solve the problem, is to find a way to show your solution on paper.

MATH WORKSHOP

2 Addition and Subtraction: Story Problems and Games

15–30 MIN

Ask all students to begin with the story problem on *Student Activity Book* page 63. Explain that as they finish they can choose among three other activities.

2A How Many Balls?

INDIVIDUALS

Students solve a story problem about combining and record their work.

ONGOING ASSESSMENT: Observing Students at Work

Students solve a story problem about combining two amounts and find a way to show their solution on paper.❷

- **Can students make sense of the action of the problem?** What strategies do they use to find a solution? Do they act it out? Model it with manipulatives? Use their fingers? Do they count all? Count on? Use number combinations they know?

- **How do students record their work?** Do they use pictures of balls or of the counters they used to solve the problem? Do they use numbers? Words? An equation? Do students simply show 5, or do they attempt to show how they solved the problem, perhaps indicating the action or labeling the groups or the individual items?

As you observe, note students who used different methods of recording their work to inform the discussion at the end of this session.

DIFFERENTIATION: Supporting the Range of Learners

Intervention Meet with students who have difficulty getting started. Follow the routine you have been using with the whole class: read the problem aloud, encourage students to visualize and retell the story, and then have them act it out or represent it with cubes. Reviewing the *Student Math Handbook Flip Chart* may also help.

Intervention Help students who struggle with what to show on paper, or how to show what they did on paper, to think about what they could draw (e.g., pictures of the balls in the problem or pictures of the cubes they used to solve the problem) or write (e.g., words or numbers). For example, "I see that you drew a picture of the swings here. How many balls did Yoshio find by the swings?" Or, "You said that the first thing you did was to take three cubes for the balls near the swings. Could you draw a picture that shows the three cubes? What did you do next?"

2B Build and Remove

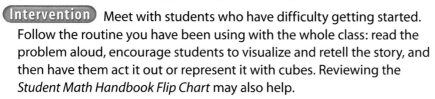

PAIRS

For complete details on this activity, see Session 3.4, pages 116–117.

2C Double Compare

PAIRS

For complete details on this activity, see Session 3.2, page 106.

2D Roll and Record 3

INDIVIDUALS

For complete details on this activity, see Session 3.1, pages 101–102.

Teaching Note

❷ **Assembling a Portfolio** In Sessions 3.5–3.7, students solve story problems and show how they solved them on paper. As you observe, look for pieces of work to add to students' portfolios in order to demonstrate how they are making sense of and solving such problems and recording their thinking.

DISCUSSION

10 MIN CLASS

③ How Did You Record?

Math Focus Points for Discussion

◆ Using numbers, pictures, and/or words to represent a solution to a problem

Introduce this discussion by solving the problem together as a class. Once the class is in agreement about the answer, focus on how students recorded their work.

It sounds as if you all agree that [Yoshio] found five balls. I am interested in what you wrote or drew on your papers . . . [Kiyo] says she drew three circles and then two more circles to show the balls. Then she counted them. Did anyone else do something similar to [Kiyo]? . . . Who did it another way? I noticed that [Abby's] paper only has numbers on it.

In this way, highlight the different methods you observed students using as they worked. Some students draw elaborate pictures no matter what the context (e.g., a detailed drawing of the playground); others draw only the balls or pictures of the manipulatives they used to stand for the balls (e.g., cubes or buttons). Some students use tallies or pictures of their fingers. Others use numbers, and a few may use addition notation and even an equation. Some use a combination of these methods. Note that some students' work also indicates *how* they solved the problem in some way—e.g., labeling each ball from 1–5, using arrows to show the joining action, or labeling each group and the whole with the totals (2, 3, and 5).

After a few students have shared, have students pair up and explain their work to their partners. Encourage them to explain how they used pictures or what the numbers on their papers mean. In this way every student in the class will have the opportunity to verbally describe their work to someone.

SESSION FOLLOW-UP

④ Homework

 Family Letter: Send home copies of the Family Letter (M19–M20) with each student.

How Do You Show the One That Is Gone?

Math Focus Points

◆ Modeling the action of combining and separating situations

◆ Developing strategies for solving addition and subtraction story problems

◆ Using numbers, pictures, and/or words to represent a solution to a problem

Today's Plan		Materials
ACTIVITY **①** **Introducing How Many Grapes?**	5 MIN CLASS	• *Student Activity Book,* p. 64
MATH WORKSHOP **②** **Addition and Subtraction: Story Problems and Games** **2A** *How Many Grapes?* **2B** *Build and Remove* **2C** *Double Compare* **2D** *Roll and Record 3*	15–30 MIN	**2A** • *Student Activity Book,* p. 64 • Cubes or other counters **2B** • Materials from Session 3.4, p. 115 **2C** • Materials from Sessions 3.2, p. 105 **2D** • Materials from Session 3.1, p. 100
DISCUSSION **③** **How Do You Show the One That Is Gone?**	10 MIN CLASS	• Completed copy of *Student Activity Book,* p. 64
SESSION FOLLOW-UP **④** **Practice**		• *Student Math Handbook Flip Chart,* pp. 30, 31, 32, 33, 34

Classroom Routines

Calendar: What's Missing? Remove three dates on the monthly calendar. Challenge students to tell you which cards are missing and how they know.

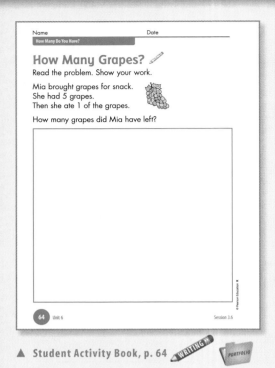

Name _____ Date _____

How Many Do You Have?

How Many Grapes?
Read the problem. Show your work.

Mia brought grapes for snack.
She had 5 grapes.
Then she ate 1 of the grapes.

How many grapes did Mia have left?

64   Unit 6   Session 3.6

▲ **Student Activity Book, p. 64**

ACTIVITY

1 Introducing How Many Grapes?

5 MIN   CLASS

Explain that today's session will be just like yesterday's. You will tell and discuss a story, and then students will solve it and record their work.

[Mia] brought grapes for snack. She had five grapes. Then she ate one of the grapes.

As usual, ask several students to retell the story in their own words, even if one student tells the story correctly the first time. Encourage students to focus on the actions of the story rather than what they think the question and answer will be.

Just like we did yesterday, I'm going to ask a question about the story, and then I'd like you to solve it and find a way to show your solution on paper.

Show them *Student Activity Book* page 64, read it aloud, and explain the strategies and materials available to them.

So the question you'll be thinking about is how many grapes did [Mia] have left? Remember she had five grapes, and she ate one. You can use any of the strategies we've been using to solve it—you can act it out, talk with a partner, or model it with cubes or counters. Drawing a picture might help, too.

MATH WORKSHOP

2 Addition and Subtraction: Story Problems and Games

15–30 MIN

Ask all students to begin with the story problem on *Student Activity Book* page 64. Explain that, as they finish, they can choose among the following activities.

2A How Many Grapes?

INDIVIDUALS

Students solve a story problem about separating one amount from another and then record their work.

ONGOING ASSESSMENT: Observing Students at Work

Students solve a story problem about separating one amount from another and find a way to show their solutions on paper.

- **Can students make sense of the action of the problem?** What strategies do they use to find a solution? Do they act it out? Model it with manipulatives? Use their fingers? Do they remove one and count the ones that remain? Count back?

- **How do students record their work?** Do they use pictures of grapes or of the counters they use to solve the problem? Do they use numbers? Words? A combination? Do students simply show the end result, four, or do they attempt to show the action of the problem?

For many students, finding a way to show a grape that is gone is quite challenging. As you observe, note the different ways students handle this to use in the discussion at the end of this session.

DIFFERENTIATION: Supporting the Range of Learners

Intervention Meet with students who have difficulty getting started. Follow the routine you have been using with the whole class: read the problem aloud, encourage students to visualize and retell the story, and then have them act it out or represent it with cubes.

Intervention Help students who struggle with what to show on paper, or how to show what they did on paper, to think about what they could draw (e.g., pictures of the grapes in the problem or pictures of the cubes they used to solve the problem) or write (e.g., words or numbers). For example, "I see that you drew a picture of [Mia] here. How many grapes did [Mia] have?" Or, "You said that the first thing you did was take five cubes for the grapes [Mia] had for snack. Could you draw a picture that shows the five cubes? What did you do next?"

2B Build and Remove
PAIRS

For complete details on this activity, see Session 3.4, pages 116–117.

2C Double Compare
PAIRS

For complete details on this activity, see Session 3.2, page 106.

2D *Roll and Record 3*

INDIVIDUALS

For complete details on this activity, see Session 3.1, pages 101–102.

DISCUSSION

10 MIN   CLASS

3 How Do You Show the One That Is Gone?

Math Focus Points for Discussion

◆ Using numbers, pictures, and/or words to represent a solution to a problem

Introduce this discussion by solving the problem together as a class. Once the class is in agreement about the answer, focus on how students recorded their work.

It sounds like you all agree that [Mia] had four grapes left at the end of the story. I am interested in what you wrote or drew on your papers.

Most likely, some students recorded the situation at the end of the story, drawing or representing four grapes.

[Brad] says he drew four [circles, cubes], to show the four grapes that were left. Raise your hand if you did something like [Brad].

Discuss several different representations—circles for grapes, squares for the cubes that stood for grapes, the number 4. Then, point out the challenging aspect of recording one's work for a subtraction problem.

When I look at these papers, I can see really clearly that there were four grapes left at the end of the story. But I don't see the five grapes that [Mia] started with, or the one grape that she ate. [Raul] and I were talking about this—how do you show something that went away? It's really tricky.

Ask volunteers who showed more than a picture of the situation at the end of the story to share their work.

So [Raul] drew a picture of [Mia] eating that one grape, [Tammy] drew five grapes and then crossed one of the grapes out, and [Latoya] drew an arrow from one of the grapes to [Mia's] mouth to show that she ate one of the grapes.

In this way, highlight the different methods you observed students using as they worked.

After a few students have shared, have students pair up and explain their work to their partners. Encourage them to explain how they used pictures or what the numbers on their papers mean. In this way every student in the class will have the opportunity to verbally describe their work to someone.

SESSION FOLLOW-UP
Practice

Student Math Handbook Flip Chart: Use the *Student Math Handbook Flip Chart* pages 30, 31, 32, 33, 34. to reinforce concepts from today's session. See pages 189–193 in the back of this unit.

How Many Blocks?

Math Focus Points

◆ Modeling the action of combining and separating situations

◆ Developing strategies for solving addition and subtraction story problems

◆ Using numbers, pictures, and/or words to represent a solution to a problem

Today's Plan		Materials
① ACTIVITY **Introducing How Many Blocks?**	🕐 👥 5 MIN CLASS	• *Student Activity Book,* p. 65
② MATH WORKSHOP **Addition and Subtraction: Story Problems and Games** ㉒ How Many Blocks? ㉓ *Build and Remove* ㉔ *Double Compare* ㉕ *Roll and Record 3*	🕐 15–30 MIN	㉒ • *Student Activity Book,* p. 65 • Cubes or other counters ㉓ • Materials from Session 3.4, p. 115 ㉔ • Materials from Session 3.2, p. 105 ㉕ • Materials from Session 3.1, p. 100
③ DISCUSSION **How Did You Record?**	🕐 👥 10 MIN CLASS	• Completed copy of *Student Activity Book,* p. 65
④ SESSION FOLLOW-UP **Practice**		• *Student Math Handbook Flip Chart,* pp. 31, 32, 33, 34

Classroom Routines

Patterns on the Pocket Chart: What Comes Here? Arrange an AB repeating pattern on the first two rows of the pocket chart using square tiles (blue, red). Cover the eighth through the last square tile with Question Mark Cards. Follow the basic *Patterns* activity but instead of asking for the *next* color in the pattern sequence, point to the tenth pocket and ask students what color is under the Question Mark Card. Students hold up the color tile they think it is.

ACTIVITY

Introducing How Many Blocks?

5 MIN   CLASS

Explain that today will be just like Sessions 3.5 and 3.6—you will tell and discuss a story, and then students will solve it and record their work.

[Jack] was building with blocks. He used two blocks to build a wall. He used four blocks to build a bridge.

As usual, ask several students to retell the story in their own words, even if one student tells the story correctly the first time. Encourage students to focus on the actions of the story rather than on what they think the question and answer will be.

Just like we've been doing, I'm going to ask a question about the story, and then I'd like you to solve it and find a way to show your solution on paper.

Show them *Student Activity Book* page 65, read it aloud, and explain the strategies and materials available to them.

The question you'll be thinking about is how many blocks did [Jack] use? Remember he used two to make a wall, and four to make a bridge. You can use any of the strategies we've been using to solve it— you can act it out, talk with a partner, or model it with cubes or counters. Drawing a picture might help, too.

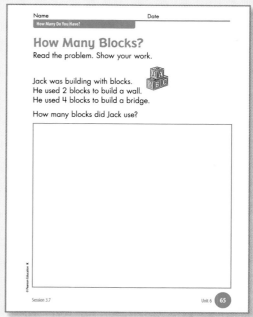

▲ Student Activity Book, p. 65

MATH WORKSHOP

Addition and Subtraction: Story Problems and Games

15–30 MIN

Have all students begin Math Workshop with the story problem on *Student Activity Book* page 65. Explain that, as they finish they can choose from the other four activities.

2A How Many Blocks?

INDIVIDUALS

Students solve a story problem about combining and record their work.

ONGOING ASSESSMENT: Observing Students at Work

Students solve a story problem about combining two amounts and find a way to show their solutions on paper.

- **Can students make sense of the action of the problem?** What strategies do they use to find a solution? Do they act it out? Model it with manipulatives? Use their fingers? Do they count all? Count on? Use number combinations they know?

- **How do students record their work?** Do they use pictures of blocks or of the counters they used to solve the problem? Do they use numbers? Words? Symbols? An equation? Do students simply show six, or do they attempt to show the action of the problem and how they solved the problem, perhaps indicating the action or labeling the groups or the individual items?

Again, focus your observations on the different methods students use to record their work and bring these up at the discussion at the end of this session.

DIFFERENTIATION: Supporting the Range of Learners

Intervention Meet with students who have difficulty getting started. Follow the routine you have been using with the whole class: read the problem aloud, encourage students to visualize and retell the story, and have them act it out or represent it with cubes.

Intervention Help students who struggle with what to show on paper, or how to show what they did on paper, to think about what they could draw or write. Also, remind them of the strategies discussed in the last two sessions.

2B *Build and Remove*

PAIRS

For complete details on this activity, see Session 3.4, pages 116–117.

2C *Double Compare*

PAIRS

For complete details on this activity, see Session 3.2, page 106.

2D *Roll and Record 3*

INDIVIDUALS

For complete details on this activity, see Session 3.1, pages 101–102.

DISCUSSION

③ How Did You Record?

10 MIN   CLASS

Math Focus Points for Discussion

◆ Using numbers, pictures, and/or words to represent a solution to a problem

Introduce this discussion by solving the problem together as a class. Once the class is in agreement about the answer, focus on how students recorded their work. As you did in Sessions 3.5 and 3.6, highlight the different methods you observed students using as they worked, and then, after a few volunteers have shared, have students pair up and explain their work to their partners. Encourage them to explain how they used pictures or what the numbers on their papers mean. In this way every student in the class will have the opportunity to verbally describe his or her work to someone.

SESSION FOLLOW-UP

④ Practice

Student Math Handbook Flip Chart: Use the *Student Math Handbook Flip Chart* pages 31, 32, 33, 34 to reinforce concepts from today's session. See pages 189–193 in the back of this unit.

Mathematical Emphases

Whole Number Operations Making sense of and developing strategies to solve addition and subtraction problems with small numbers

Math Focus Points

◆ Finding combinations of five and six

◆ Decomposing numbers in different ways

◆ Considering combinations of a number (e.g., 6 is 3 and 3 and also 5 and 1)

◆ Combining two single-digit numbers, with totals to 20

Whole Number Operations Using manipulatives, drawings, tools, and notation to show strategies and solutions

Math Focus Points

◆ Using numbers, pictures, and/or words to represent a quantity or a solution to a problem

◆ Using numbers, and/or addition notation, to record how many and to represent an addition situation

This Investigation also focuses on

◆ Beginning to recognize that some problems have more than one solution

How Many of Each?

	Student Activity Book	Student Math Handbook Flip Chart	Professional Development: Read Ahead of Time	
SESSION 4.1 p. 138				
Five Crayons in All Students solve a problem in which they have five crayons altogether, some blue and some red. They determine one or more combinations of blue and red crayons that they could have to make up five in all, and then they share their solutions with the class.	66	27	• **Algebra Connections in this Unit,** p. 18 • **Teacher Note:** How Students Approach Five Crayons in All, p. 179; When the Teacher Records Students' Solutions, p. 182	
SESSION 4.2 p. 143				
Combinations of Six Students revisit two games about combinations of numbers—*Toss the Chips* and *Racing Bears*. Class discussion focuses on combinations of 6.		28, 29		
SESSION 4.3 p. 146				
Total of Six Students learn and play a new game called *Total of Six*, in which they find combinations that make 6 in a displayed set of Primary Number Cards.	67	28, 29		
SESSION 4.4 p. 151				
Six Crayons in All Students solve another How Many of Each? problem, finding and sharing combinations of red and blue crayons, with six crayons in all.	68	28, 29		

Classroom Routines See page 20 for an overview.

Attendance	Patterns on the Pocket Chart
• Attendance Stick	• Pocket Chart(s)
Today's Question	• M7, Question Mark Cards (from Investigation 1)
• Stick-on notes (1 per student)	• M14, Arrow Cards (from Investigation 3)
• *Today's Question* charts for Sessions 4.2 and 4.6.	**Calendar**
See instructions on pages 143 and 159.	• Class calendar or class pocket calendar

Materials to Gather	Materials to Prepare
• **Blue and red crayons** (5 of each) • **Empty crayon box** (optional) • **Blue and red crayons or cubes** (5 of each per student) • **Red and blue crayons, markers, or colored pencils** • **Chart paper** (optional)	
• **Materials for** *Toss the Chips* See Session 1.2. • **Materials for** *Racing Bears* See Session 1.5.	• **Chart paper** On chart paper draw the *Toss the Chips* table (M2).
• **Tower of 6 cubes** (1 per student) • **Materials for** *Toss the Chips* See Session 1.2. • **Materials for** *Racing Bears* See Session 1.5. • **Primary Number Cards** (with 7–10 and Wild Cards removed; 3 sets per pair)	• **M22,** *Total of Six* **Gameboard** Make copies. (1 per pair)
• **Crayons or cubes** (6 red and 6 blue per student) • **Red and blue crayons, markers, or colored pencils** • **Materials for** *Toss the Chips* See Session 1.2. • **Materials for** *Racing Bears* See Session 1.5. • **Materials for** *Total of Six* See Session 4.3. • **Chart paper** Write title "Six Crayons in All".	

How Many of Each?, *continued*

	Student Activity Book	Student Math Handbook Flip Chart	Professional Development: Read Ahead of Time	
SESSION 4.5 p. 155				
More Combinations of Six and End-of-Unit Assessment Class begins with a discussion about finding combinations of 6. Then, while Math Workshop continues, students who have not yet met the benchmarks for this unit meet individually with the teacher. Depending on which benchmarks they have or have not met, they count a set of 20 objects, solve some story problems, or play a few rounds of *Roll and Record 3* with the teacher.	69		• **Teacher Note:** Observing Kindergarteners as They Count, p. 165; Counting Is More Than 1, 2, 3, p. 166; Assessing Addition, p. 168	
SESSION 4.6 p. 159				
End-of-Unit Assessment and Combinations of Six Math Workshop continues, while students who have not yet met the benchmarks meet individually with the teacher. Class discussion focuses on combinations of 6.		28, 29		

Materials to Gather	Materials to Prepare
• **Tower of 6 Cubes** (1 per student) • **Chart paper** Write title "Total of Six". • **Completed and blank copies of Assessment Checklists M5, M6, M12** ✓ • **20 cubes** • **0-to-5 dot cube** (2) • **Materials for** *Total of Six* See Session 4.3. • **Materials for** *Toss the Chips* See Session 1.2. • **Materials for** *Racing Bears* See Session 1.5.	• **M13,** *Roll and Record 3* **Recording Sheet** Make copies. (as needed)
• **Materials for End-of-Unit Assessments** See Session 4.5. • **Materials for** *Toss the Chips* See Session 1.2. • **Materials for** *Racing Bears* See Session 1.5. • **Materials for** *Totals of Six* See Session 4.3. • **Charts: "Toss the Chips"** (from Session 4.2), **"Six Crayons in All"** (from Session 4.4), **and "Total of Six"** (from Session 4.5)	

✓ Checklist Available

Five Crayons in All

Math Focus Points

◆ Finding combinations of five

◆ Using numbers, pictures, and/or words to represent a solution to a problem

◆ Beginning to recognize that some problems have more than one solution

Today's Plan		Materials
ACTIVITY **❶ Introducing Five Crayons in All**	🕙 10 MIN 👥 CLASS	• *Student Activity Book,* p. 66 • Blue and red crayons; empty crayon box (optional)
ACTIVITY **❷ Five Crayons in All**	🕙 10–25 MIN 🧍 INDIVIDUALS 👥 PAIRS	• *Student Activity Book,* p. 66 • Red and blue crayons or cubes; colored pencils; crayons or markers
DISCUSSION **❸ Five Crayons in All**	🕙 10 MIN 👥 CLASS	• Completed copy of *Student Activity Book,* p. 66 • Crayons or cubes; chart paper (optional)
SESSION FOLLOW-UP **❹ Practice**		• *Student Math Handbook Flip Chart,* p. 27

Classroom Routines

Attendance: How Many Have Counted? **Count around the circle as usual but pause several times during the count to ask students how many people have counted so far and how they know. Help students see why the number they say represents the number of students who have counted so far and that the last number represents the total number of students in class today.**

ACTIVITY

1 Introducing Five Crayons in All

 10 MIN CLASS

To introduce this How Many of Each? problem, ❶ hold up several blue and red crayons and an empty crayon box that holds at least five crayons.

I want to put five crayons in my box. I want to have a mix of blue and red crayons, so I need some blue ones and some red ones. How many of each color could I have? How many blues? How many reds? Remember, I need five crayons in all.

Accept two different suggestions and model them with crayons. If some students disagree with the solutions their classmates offer, ask them to explain their thinking, but keep the discussion brief and the focus on explaining the task clearly enough so that students will be able to work on finding solutions on their own.

Hmm, so it seems there is more than one solution to this problem about five blue and red crayons. Your job today is to find different ways to solve the problem, and then use pictures, or numbers, or both, to show your solution(s).

Show students *Student Activity Book* page 66 and explain what materials (crayons, cubes, counters) are available. Encourage students to work in pairs and to share their ideas with each other.

 ACTIVITY

2 Five Crayons in All

 10–25 MIN INDIVIDUALS PAIRS

Students work alone or in pairs to find at least one combination of five red and blue crayons, and record their work on *Student Activity Book* page 66. ❷

ONGOING ASSESSMENT: Observing Students at Work

Students solve a complex problem, find combinations of a number, and keep track of and record their work.

- **How do students solve the problem?** Do they randomly assemble a group of five counters using some red and some blue? Do they use a more systematic approach, adjusting one solution to find another? Do they count up from the number of [red] to figure out how many [blue] they need? Do any use knowledge of number combinations? ❸ ❹

Math Note

❶ **How Many of Each? Problems** Five Crayons in All is an example of a type of problem called How Many of Each? that students solve in this Investigation and throughout first grade. A basic How Many of Each? problem gives students two types of objects (such as red and blue crayons) and a total number (in this case, five). Students determine how many of each they could have to make up the total. These problems give students repeated practice with counting, combining, and finding number combinations, and also with recording and organizing solutions.

Teaching Note

❷ **Assembling a Portfolio** Students solve a How Many of Each? problem in this session and again in Session 4.4. Choose one of these pieces of work to add to students' portfolios, to show how they are making sense of and solving a complex problem, and to demonstrate their growing ability to represent their thinking on paper.

Professional Development

❸ **Teacher Note:** How Students Approach Five Crayons in All, p. 179

Algebra Note

❹ **Using One Solution to Find Another** Some students adapt one solution to create another, for example, trading one red crayon for one blue. Encourage students to describe such strategies, to think about what would happen if they continue to use that strategy, and to consider the relationship between the solutions (e.g., 4 and 1 becomes 3 and 2; 3 and 2 becomes 2 and 3).

Teaching Note

⑤ **More Than One Solution** Encourage students to seek more than one solution if you think they are ready, but do not insist that they do so. Some students may be sufficiently challenged by finding just one solution.

▲ **Student Activity Book, p. 66**

- **Do students find more than one solution?** Do they recognize repeated solutions?⑤

- **How do students record their solutions?** Do they use pictures? Numbers? Words? Notation? Some combination of these? Do they keep track of the number of blue crayons, the number of red crayons, and the number in all? Do their representations accurately convey their solutions?

Sample Student Work

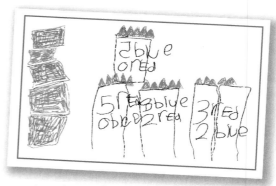

Sample Student Work

Sample Student Work

As you observe, note the strategies students use to record their work so that you can use them to record during the discussion at the end of this session.

DIFFERENTIATION: Supporting the Range of Learners

Intervention Encourage students who have difficulty getting started to use crayons or counters to model the problem. Offer assistance without showing them a solution. For example, put out two or three blue counters, explain that they stand for blue crayons, and then ask the student to figure out how many red crayons are needed. Or, you might put out six or seven counters in any combination of two colors and ask students to adjust the number of counters to make five in all.

Intervention Students who have difficulty coordinating and keeping track of the parts of the problem, might do better to solve the problem with a total of just four or three crayons so that they can focus on the goal of the problem and on relationships between the total and the two parts that make up the total. If any students record just the number in each group, ask them to clarify their solutions:

How can we tell if that 2 means two red crayons or two blue ones?

Extension Encourage students who find and record a solution before others are finished, to share their work with a partner. They can also look for additional solutions or take on the challenge of trying to find them all.

ELL Students will need to understand the phrase *how many* in order to solve How Many of Each? problems. English Language Learners will acquire this language through repeated modeling and practice. Think aloud as you work on problems with the children. *How many* crayons do we need altogether? Let's see *how many* blue crayons we have. *How many* red crayons do we need to make 5? To develop students' English-speaking skills, encourage them to think aloud as they solve the problems.

DISCUSSION

10 MIN   **CLASS**

③ Five Crayons in All

Math Focus Points for Discussion

◆ Finding combinations of five

Professional Development

 Teacher Note: When the Teacher Records Students' Solutions, p. 182

When everyone has found at least one solution, call students together with their papers to share some of their solutions.

Ask one student to explain his or her solution. Ask another student to use crayons (or cubes or other counters) to model the solution for the class. Then, ask others to tell whether they got the same solution. In this way you acknowledge the work of many students.

Does anyone have a solution to share? [Carmen] got [four blue] crayons and [one red one]. Raise your hand if you found [four blue and one red]. Did anyone get something different?

Record the solutions on chart paper or on the board. Use a method of recording that you saw students using as they worked on the problem.

As your list of solutions grows, remind students that you are looking for combinations of blue and red crayons that are not yet recorded. Encourage students to look carefully at the list and at their own work to find new combinations.

So, I'm noticing that we have a solution that uses [one red] and [four blue] and we have another solution that uses [three reds] and [two blues]. Did anyone use [two red] crayons?

If no one offers a solution ask students to solve the problem.

Take a minute to think about this problem. If we had [two red] crayons, how many [blue] crayons could we put in the box so that we would have five crayons in all?

The session may or may not end with every possible combination being shared and posted on the chart. The purpose of this discussion is not to generate all possible combinations but instead to heighten students' awareness that some problems can have more than one solution. As students work with more How Many of Each? problems in this Investigation and throughout first grade, the focus will shift to finding all possible combinations.

SESSION FOLLOW-UP

④ Practice

Student Math Handbook Flip Chart: Use the *Student Math Handbook Flip Chart* page 27 to reinforce concept's from today's session. See pages 189–193 in the back of this unit.

Combinations of Six

Math Focus Points

◆ Decomposing numbers in different ways

◆ Using numbers to record how many

◆ Considering combinations of a number
   (e.g., 6 is 3 and 3 and also 5 and 1)

Today's Plan		Materials
MATH WORKSHOP **❶ Combinations of Six** **1A** *Toss the Chips* **1B** *Racing Bears*	20–35 MIN	**1A** • Materials from Session 1.2, p. 35 **1B** • Materials from Session 1.5, p. 50
DISCUSSION **❷ Combinations of Six**	10 MIN CLASS	• Chart paper* • Completed copy of M2
SESSION FOLLOW-UP **❸ Practice**		• *Student Math Handbook Flip Chart,* pp. 28, 29

*See *Materials to Prepare*, p. 135.

Classroom Routines

Today's Question: Have you ever eaten watermelon? On chart paper, create a horizontal table titled "Have you ever eaten watermelon?" with the heading "Yes" written at the left of the top row and "No" written at the left of the bottom row. Students respond by writing their names on stick-on notes and sticking them in the appropriate row. Count the responses as a class and discuss what the results of the survey tell you.

MATH WORKSHOP

Combinations of Six

20–35 MIN

In preparation for upcoming sessions about combinations of six, students revisit *Racing Bears* and *Toss the Chips*. Explain that students will revisit these games, and remind them what each activity entails, what materials are required, and where they are located. Explain that pairs need to play one round of *Toss the Chips* with six chips by the end of this Math Workshop, to be ready for the discussion at the end of this session.

1A Toss the Chips

PAIRS

For complete details on this activity, see Session 1.2, page 36.

1B Racing Bears

PAIRS

For complete details on this activity, see Sessions 1.5, pages 51–53.

DIFFERENTIATION: Supporting the Range of Learners

Extension Challenge students to collect as many counters as they can on each turn. In other words, encourage them to think about how to split a roll among different bears on different tracks.

DISCUSSION

Combinations of Six

10 MIN   CLASS

Math Focus Points for Discussion

◆ Considering combinations of a number (e.g., 6 is 3 and 3 and also 5 and 1)

Post the chart paper table you made. Ask students to refer to their completed *Toss the Chips* Recording Sheet from when they played with six chips.

Let's make a list of some of the ways the counters landed when you tossed six chips. [Emma] says she got four red and two yellow. Does that equal six? How do you know?

Encourage students to explain how they know that four red and two yellow equals six counters. Students may count the chips, count on their fingers, or know that $4 + 2$ equals 6. Model each strategy that students suggest.

Everyone look at your paper. Raise your hand if you got four red and two yellow, too.❶

Record each combination. As you do, ask a volunteer to model the suggestion with counters, to help students develop visual images of combinations of 6.

Lots of people got four red and two yellow. I am going to write that on our chart. [Ricardo], could you show us what that would look like with the counters?

Then, ask students to check their papers for a different combination.

[Emma] got four red and two yellow. Who got that? Who got something different?

Encourage students to check their papers for ways that are not already recorded, but know that kindergarteners are likely to suggest combinations that have already been shared.❷

Continue until there are no new combinations to share. Because the probability of throwing all red, or all yellow, is very small, students may not have six and zero or zero and six as possible combinations. If this combination has not come up, ask students about it.

Did anyone toss the chips and have *all* of the chips land on the same color? No one? Do you think it's possible to get *all* red or *all* yellow?

End with an open-ended question.

Do you think we have *all* of the ways to make six with red and yellow counters? Do you think there are other ways? You might think about this question the next time you play *Toss the Chips*.

Explain that you will post the chart so that students can refer to it over the next few sessions and add any new combinations of six that they find. (This poster will *also* be used during the discussion at the end of Session 4.6.)

SESSION FOLLOW-UP

③ Practice

 Student Math Handbook Flip Chart: Use the *Student Math Handbook Flip Chart* pages 28, 29 to reinforce concepts from today's session. See pages 189–193 in the back of this unit.

Teaching Note

❶ **Engaging All Students** Asking students to check for a solution encourages them to pay attention to the conversation, to listen to each other, and to reflect on their work. It also allows many students to engage in the conversation without every student sharing one by one.

Algebra Note

❷ **"Opposites"** Some students notice particular pairs of combinations (e.g., 2 red and 4 yellow and 4 red and 2 yellow) and name them "opposites." Ask these students what they mean, and challenge them to find other opposites for the number 6. (See **Algebra Connections in This Unit,** p. 18.)

Total of Six

Math Focus Points

- Finding combinations of six
- Combining two single-digit numbers, with totals to 6
- Using numbers, and/or addition notation, to record how many and to represent an addition situation

Today's Plan		Materials
ACTIVITY **①Introducing** *Total of Six* 5–10 MIN CLASS		• Primary Number Cards (with 7–10 and Wild Cards removed)* • M22* • Tower of 6 cubes
MATH WORKSHOP **②More Combinations of Six** **2A** *Total of Six* **2B** *Toss the Chips* **2C** *Racing Bears* 20–30 MIN		**2A** • Materials from Activity 1 **2B** • Materials from Session 1.2, p. 35 **2C** • Materials from Session 1.5, p. 50
DISCUSSION **③Checking In** 5 MIN CLASS		
SESSION FOLLOW-UP **④Practice**		• *Student Activity Book,* p. 67

*See *Materials to Prepare,* p. 135.

Classroom Routines

Calendar: Mixed Up Calendar Choose two date cards and change their position on the calendar so that they are out of order. Challenge students to find the mistakes and help you fix them.

ACTIVITY

1 Introducing *Total of Six*

5–10 MIN   CLASS

To introduce *Total of Six,* play a demonstration game with a volunteer. Give each student a tower of six cubes and then lay out twelve cards (three rows, four cards per row) on the *Total of Six* Gameboard (M22). Numbers should be facing up, turned so that students can read them. Put the remaining cards in a pile, facedown.

Explain that in this game, players look for combinations that total six, using any number of cards. They will take turns finding one combination at a time. As you play the demonstration game, ask questions that will involve students in your turn.

Does anyone see some cards I could put together to make six? (If students need help, find a pair that totals six and point to one of those cards.) What if I want to use this 4? Is there a card I could put together with this 4 to make six?

Encourage students to explain how they figured out what number to add to four to make six. If no one suggests using the cube tower, bring it up yourself.

How could your cube tower help us figure that how many to add to four to make six?

Count a tower of six cubes by 1s, and then use it to model students' suggestions.

So [Lionel's] tower has 1, 2, 3, 4, 5, 6 cubes in it. [Lionel] counted 1, 2, 3, 4 (break off four cubes, in one chunk) and broke the tower into two parts. Why did Lionel count to 4? *(Because the problem was 4 + ? = 6)*

Then [Lionel] had two towers. One tower had four, just like on the number card. And the other tower had [hold up tower of two cubes] two cubes. So four cubes plus two cubes [join the two towers back into one] equals how many cubes? . . . six. 1, 2, 3, 4, 5, 6.

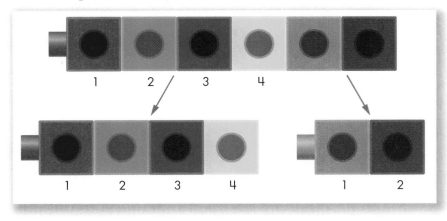

Once students agree that you have found a combination of 6, ask them to help you write an equation for it.

After you find cards that go together to make 6, you write an equation *that shows your* combination. *How would I write an equation that shows that 4 and 2 make 6?*

$$4 + 2 = 6 \qquad 2 + 4 = 6$$
$$6 = 4 + 2 \qquad 6 = 2 + 4$$

Finally, explain that, after finding and recording a combination that makes six, the player removes those cards (the 4 and the 2), and replaces them with cards from the top of the deck.

Now it's [Victor's] turn. What is [Victor] trying to do?

Review the goals and steps of the game as you continue your sample game. Offer hints if your volunteer does not readily find a combination of six.

Let's say [Victor] wants to use this 5. Is there another card he could put together with the 5 to make six?

Again, discuss strategies for figuring this out, and model how to use an equation to record. Remove and replace the cards used.

If no one suggests using more than two cards to make 6, do this on your next turn.

Suppose I wanted to make six using more than two cards. Can any one find a combination of three cards that total six? What if I chose the 2 and the 1. What card could I choose that would make six?

Point out that a 0 card may be included in any combination such as 0 + 6 or 4 + 2 + 0. Play continues until no more combinations of six can be made. Players may occasionally be able to use all of the cards, but often there will be several left.

MATH WORKSHOP

2 **More Combinations of Six**

20–30 MIN

Explain that three activities are available during Math Workshop. Remind students what each activity entails, what materials are required, and where they are located. Ask every pair to try at least one game of *Total of Six*.

2A *Total of Six*

PAIRS

Partners take turns finding combinations of two or more numbers that total six in a 3-by-4 array of Primary Number Cards. When they find a combination that totals six, they take the cards, replace them with new cards, and use addition notation to record the combination.

ONGOING ASSESSMENT: Observing Students at Work

Students find combinations of two or more numbers that total six and use addition notation to record them.

- **What strategies do students use as they play?** Do they work randomly, choosing a number to start with and combining it with different numbers to find a way to make six? Do they look for particular combinations? Do they know how many more they need to make six given one card? Given two cards?

- **How do students figure out the total amounts?** Do they count all from 1 each time? Count up from one of the numbers? Use knowledge of number combinations?

- **How do students determine that the game is over?** Do they keep trying combinations of remaining cards to make six?

DIFFERENTIATION: Supporting the Range of Learners

Intervention Some students may benefit from playing in a small group with you, and seeing how a tower of 6 cubes can help them find 2-addend combinations of six. Some may benefit from playing the same game, but with a smaller total, such as four or five. If you do this, adjust the cards included in the deck so that the total students are making is the largest card. For example, if students are playing *Total of Four,* they will need the cards 0–4.

Teaching Note

① Preparing for the End-of-Unit Assessment
Before Session 4.5, gather the assessment checklists you have filled in over the course of this unit: Assessment Checklist: Writing Numbers to 10 (M5), Assessment Checklist: Counting (M6), and Assessment Checklist: Addition (M12). For each benchmark, look over your notes, and sort students into three categories: those who have clearly met the benchmark, those who have not yet met the benchmark, and those you have questions about. You will be meeting with the students in the latter two categories over the course of Sessions 4.5 and 4.6. You do not need to meet with students who your notes show can consistently count a set of 20 objects accurately. Meet only with the students who your notes show have not yet demonstrated this skill, or have not done so consistently. Make a list of students you need to meet with that specifies which tasks you need to do with each student.

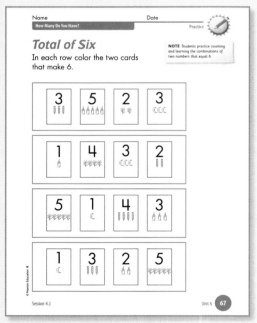

▲ Student Activity Book, p. 67

2B *Toss the Chips*
PAIRS

For complete details on this activity, see Session 1.2, page 36.

2C *Racing Bears*
PAIRS

For complete details on this activity, see Sessions 1.5, pages 51–53.

DISCUSSION
5 MIN CLASS

③ Checking In

Take this opportunity to discuss any issues that you noticed while observing students at work. The topic might be mathematical in nature, such as a strategy you'd like all students to consider (e.g., using a cube tower of 6 to play *Total of Six*) or a common error or misconception you'd like students to discuss (e.g., using addition notation incorrectly, for example writing $5 + 1 + 6$ or $5 = 1 + 6$).

It could also be a logistical issue (e.g., clarifying the rules of the game) or a management issue (e.g., being a helpful partner, working productively).

Other alternatives include checking in with students about which activities they have been choosing (e.g., "Thumbs up if you played *Total of Six* . . . *Toss the Chips* . . . *Racing Bears*."), asking everyone to hold up a piece of work, or allowing students to raise a question or make a comment about today's math class.**①**

SESSION FOLLOW-UP
④ Practice

Practice: For reinforcement of this unit's content, have students complete *Student Activity Book* page 67.

Six Crayons in All

Math Focus Points

◆ Finding combinations of six

◆ Using numbers, pictures, and/or words to represent a quantity or a solution to a problem

◆ Considering combinations of a number (e.g., 6 is 3 and 3 and also 5 and 1)

Today's Plan		Materials
ACTIVITY **❶ Introducing Six Crayons in All**	5 MIN CLASS	• *Student Activity Book,* p. 68

MATH WORKSHOP
❷ Making Six in Many Ways
  Ⓐ Six Crayons in All
  Ⓑ *Total of Six*
  Ⓒ *Toss the Chips*
  Ⓓ *Racing Bears*
	15–30 MIN	Ⓐ • *Student Activity Book,* p. 68
		   • Crayons or cubes; red and blue crayons, markers, or colored pencils
		Ⓑ • Materials from Session 4.3, p. 146
		Ⓒ • Materials from Session 1.2, p. 35
		Ⓓ • Materials from Session 1.5, p. 50

DISCUSSION **❸ Six Crayons in All**	10 MIN CLASS	• Completed copy of *Student Activity Book,* p. 68 • Chart paper*; crayons or cubes
SESSION FOLLOW-UP **❹ Practice**		• *Student Math Handbook Flip Chart,* pp. 28, 29

*See *Materials to Prepare,* p. 135.

Classroom Routines

Patterns on the Pocket Chart: What Comes Here? Arrange an AB repeating pattern on the first two rows of the pocket chart using 14 or more Arrow Cards (left, right). Cover the eighth through the last Arrow Card with Question Mark Cards. Follow the basic *Patterns* activity but instead of asking for the *next* direction in the pattern sequence, point to the twelfth pocket and ask students what direction is under the Question Mark Card. Students point in the direction they think it is.

Teaching Note

❶ **Changing the Context** You might want to adapt the context of this problem to one that is more familiar or timely for your students. Use any two related items, but keep the numbers in the problems the same. For example, if your class has been talking about pond life, the problem could be about fish and ducks; if your class often has fruit for snack, consider strawberries and bananas; if your class is learning about oceans, you might use shells and starfish. If you choose two things that are different colors or shapes and are easy to draw, students can more readily model them with counters of different colors or with pictures they draw themselves.

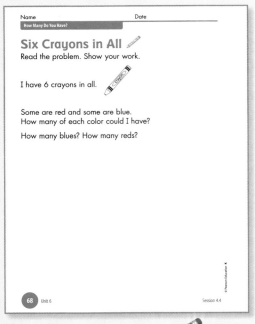

▲ Student Activity Book, p. 68

ACTIVITY
❶ Introducing Six Crayons in All

Explain that today students are going to solve another problem about blue and red crayons, but this time there are six crayons in all.❶ They record all the solutions they can find on *Student Activity Book* page 68.

MATH WORKSHOP
❷ Making Six in Many Ways

15–30 MIN

Ask everyone to begin with Six Crayons in All. When they are finished, they can choose among the other three activities.

2A Six Crayons in All

INDIVIDUALS PAIRS

Students find at least one combination of six red and blue crayons, and record their solution on *Student Activity Book* page 68.

For complete details on this activity, see Session 4.1, page 139.

Sample Student Work

DIFFERENTIATION: Supporting the Range of Learners

Intervention Some students may benefit from working on similar problems with smaller totals, such as four or five.

Extension Others may be ready for the challenge of finding several, or even all, of the possible combinations.

2B Total of Six

PAIRS

For complete details on this activity, see Session 4.3, pages 147–149.

DIFFERENTIATION: Supporting the Range of Learners

Extension Students who are playing *Total of Six* fluently could try *Total of Seven* or *Ten*. You will need to adjust the cards included in the deck so that the total students are making is the largest card. For example, if students are playing *Total of Ten,* they will need the cards 0–10.

2C Toss the Chips

PAIRS

For complete details on this activity, see Session 1.2, page 36.

2D Racing Bears

PAIRS

For complete details on this activity, see Sessions 1.5, pages 51–53.

DISCUSSION

10 MIN CLASS

3 Six Crayons in All

Math Focus Points for Discussion

◆ Considering combinations of a number (e.g., 6 is 3 and 3 and also 5 and 1)

As you did at the end of Session 4.1, call the class together to share their solutions for Six Crayons in All. Ask one student to explain a solution, and another student to model it with crayons (or cubes or other counters). Record it on chart paper, using a method you have seen students using. Ask others who found the same solution to raise their hand. As your list of solutions grows, remind students that you are looking for combinations of blue and red crayons that are not yet recorded. Encourage students to look carefully at the list, and at their own work, to find new combinations.

Teaching Notes

❷ What's the Same and What's Different? In the primary grades, debates often arise about what qualifies as a *different* combination. For example: is one blue and five red *the same as* five blues and one red? What about one blue and five red and five red and one blue? Of course, *same* or *different* depends on what you pay attention to. In the first example you get the same answer or total amount, but the number of red and blue is different. In the second example the total number *and* the number of red and blue is the same. However, when represented by two cube towers facing opposite directions, they *look* quite different. Encourage students to consider such similarities and differences, but do not expect all students to reach agreement on what qualifies as a *different* solution.

❸ Preparing for the End-of-Unit Assessment
Before Session 4.5, gather the assessment checklists you have filled in over the course of this unit: Assessment Checklist: Writing Numbers to 10 (M5), Assessment Checklist: Counting (M6), and Assessment Checklist: Addition (M12).
For each benchmark, look over your notes and sort students into three categories: those who have clearly met the benchmark, those who have not yet met the benchmark, and those you have questions about. You will be meeting with the students in the latter two categories over the course of Sessions 4.5 and 4.6. You do not need to meet with students who your notes show can consistently count a set of 20 objects accurately. Meet only with the students who your notes show have not yet demonstrated this skill or have not done so consistently. Make a list of students you need to meet with that specifies which tasks you need to do with each student.

[Lionel] got five blue crayons and one red one. I'm going to record that on our chart. [Mia], could you show us what [Lionel's] solution would look like with the the blue and red cubes? Did anyone else get five blue crayons and one red one? Raise your hands. Who got something *different?*

Some students see combinations like four blue and two red as being *different* from two red and four blue.

Encourage them to share *different* combinations, by asking:

You shared a way with four blues. When I look at our poster, I see that [Kiyo's] solution used four blues. Can you find a way that used a different number of blues?❷

Continue until there are no new combinations to share. You might end with an open-ended question:

Do you think we have all the ways to make six with red and blue crayons? Do you think there are other ways?

Explain that you will post the chart so that students can refer to it over the next few sessions, and add any new combinations of six that they find. (This poster will also be used during the discussion at the end of Session 4.6.)❸

SESSION FOLLOW-UP
Practice

Student Math Handbook Flip Chart: Use the *Student Math Handbook Flip Chart* pages 28, 29 to reinforce concepts from today's session. See pages 189–193 in the back of this unit.

More Combinations of Six and End-of-Unit Assessment

Math Focus Points

◆ Finding combinations of six

◆ Combining two single-digit numbers, with totals to 6

◆ Considering combinations of a number (e.g., 6 is 3 and 3 and also 5 and 1)

Today's Plan		Materials
DISCUSSION **① More Combinations of Six** 🕐 10 MIN 👥 CLASS		• Primary Number Cards (with 7–10 and Wild Cards removed) • Cubes; chart paper*
MATH WORKSHOP **② Combinations and Assessments** **②A** End-of-Unit Assessments **②B** *Total of Six* **②C** *Toss the Chips* **②D** *Racing Bears* 🕐 15–30 MIN		**②A** • M5*☑ ; M6*☑ ; M12*☑ ; M13 • 20 cubes; 0-to-5 dot cube **②B** • Materials from Sessions 4.3, p. 146 **②C** • Materials from Session 1.2, p. 35 **②D** • Materials from Session 1.5, p. 50
DISCUSSION **③ Checking In** 🕐 5 MIN 👥 CLASS		
SESSION FOLLOW-UP **④ Practice**		• *Student Activity Book*, p. 69

*See *Materials to Prepare*, p. 137.

Classroom Routines

Attendance: Comparing Groups Count around the circle as usual, and then count the number of students present in class and the number absent from class today. Ask students whether there are more students present or more students absent. Use the Attendance Stick to represent the situation and to model students' strategies. Challenge students to figure out how many more and discuss their strategies.

10 MIN   CLASS

Math Note

❶ **Missing Part Problems** Given one part and the whole, students must find the other part. Students will have a lot of experience solving such missing part problems in Grades 1 and 2.

DISCUSSION

❶ More Combinations of Six

Math Focus Points for Discussion

➧ Finding combinations of 6

Begin this session with a conversation about the strategies students are using to find combinations of 6 in *Total of Six*. Give each student a tower of six cubes.

I am going to turn over a Primary Number Card. Ready? What did I turn over? [5] *Okay, think quietly for a minute. If you were playing Total of Six, what number would you need to go with* [5], *to have a total of 6?*❶

Encourage students to use the cubes or their fingers to solve the problem on their own. When everyone has had a chance to solve the problem, ask several students to explain how they figured out what number to add to [5] to get six. Engage the class with those strategies by asking questions.

[Kyle] said he used his cubes. [Kyle], can you show us how you used the cubes? . . . Why did [Kyle] break off [five]?

[Jennifer] said she used her fingers. Can you show us how you used your fingers? . . . How many fingers did she put up? Why did she put up six fingers?

Model the strategies students use yourself, and ask others to do the same.

[Jennifer] explained how she used her fingers to solve the problem. [Manuel], can you show us what [Jennifer] did?

Once the class agrees on the combination of 6, ask students to help you write an equation that represents that combination, on a piece of chart paper labeled "Total of Six."

Do several more rounds as time permits, varying the numbers on the cards you lay down. Leave the chart poster hanging in the room for students to use as a reference and for use in the discussion at the end of Session 4.6.

MATH WORKSHOP

② Combinations and Assessments

15–30 MIN

Explain that three activities are available during Math Workshop.

- *Total of Six,* See Session 4.3, pages 147–149

- *Toss the Chips,* See Session 1.2, page 36

- *Racing Bears,* See Session 1.5, pages 51–53

Remind students what each activity entails, what materials are required, and where they are located. Explain that, while students are at work on these activities, you will be meeting individually with students.②

If you need another activity, present another How Many of Each? problem about six things of two types, using a new context, such as balls and bats, shoes and socks, or cars and airplanes. (Many kindergarteners will not readily see that the combinations of six they found to solve the problem in one context will also work in a different context.) Some students may be ready to tackle the challenge of a problem about seven or eight items in all, or be intrigued with finding all of the possible combinations of six blue and red crayons.

While students are working on these activities, meet individually with those you have identified as not yet meeting one or more of the benchmarks.

Benchmark 1: Write the numbers to 10.③

Play several rounds of *Roll and Record 3,* using two 0-to-5 dot cubes. Watching how students combine the results of their rolls will also help you assess Benchmark 3. Note whether students:

- Know or have a strategy for figuring out what number to write and where to write it

- Write the numbers in the correct column

Benchmark 2: Count a set of up to 20 objects. ③ ④

Give students a set of 20 loose cubes. Ask them to count them to find out how many there are. Note whether students:

- Know the names and the sequence of the numbers

- Count each object once and only once (which involves having a system for keeping track of what's been counted and what remains to be counted)

- Double-check

Teaching Note

② **Classroom Management** Review any policies you have about such a work time. For example, some teachers have an "ask three before me" rule, which requires that students ask three peers before coming to the teacher with a question.

Professional Development

③ **Teacher Note:** Observing Kindergarteners as They Count, p. 165

④ **Teacher Note:** Counting Is More Than 1, 2, 3, p. 166

Professional Development

⑤ **Teacher Note:** Assessing Addition, p. 168

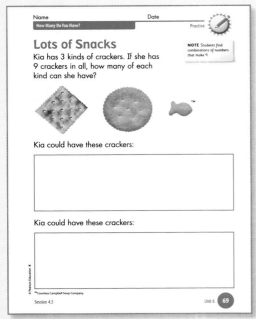

▲ Student Activity Book, p. 69

When they are finished counting, ask students how many cubes there are. Can students tell you, "20"? Or, do they recount the set to answer the question?

Benchmark 3: Combine two small quantities.⑤

Tell one of the following stories. Ask students to visualize and retell the story in their own words. Then, explain that students can use the cubes, pencil and paper, or any other tools they like to solve the problem, just as you have been doing in class.

[Mary] likes to collect rocks. One day she found four rocks in her yard. And she found two rocks at the park. How many rocks did [Mary] find?

[Jason] loves to eat cherries. At snack time, he had two cherries. [Raul] gave him three more cherries. How many cherries does [Jason] have now?

Note whether students can:

- Retell a story problem about combining groups
- Model the action of a combining story problem with manipulatives or drawings
- Accurately solve the problem

DISCUSSION

③ Checking In

5 MIN   CLASS

Take this opportunity to check in with the class. Because you have been meeting individually with students, you might want to discuss any management issues (e.g., noise level, asking a friend before asking the teacher) that arose. Or you might want to check in with students about which activities they worked on (e.g., "Thumbs up if you've finished playing *Total of Six, Toss the Chips,* or *Racing Bears*") or allow students to raise a question or make a comment about today's math class.

SESSION FOLLOW-UP

④ Practice

Practice: For enrichment, have students complete *Student Activity Book* page 69.

End-of-Unit Assessment and Combinations of Six

Math Focus Points

◆ Combining single-digit numbers with totals to 6

◆ Considering combinations of a number (e.g., 6 is 3 and 3 and also 5 and 1)

◆ Finding combinations of six

Today's Plan		Materials
MATH WORKSHOP **①** **Combinations and Assessments** **1A** End-of-Unit Assessments **1B** *Total of Six* **1C** *Toss the Chips* **1D** *Racing Bears*	20–35 MIN	**1A** • Materials from Session 4.5, p. 155 **1B** • Materials from Session 4.3, p. 146 **1C** • Materials from Session 1.2, p. 35 **1D** • Materials from Session 1.5, p. 50
DISCUSSION **②** **Combinations of Six**	10 MIN CLASS	• Charts: "Toss the Chips (from Session 4.2), "Six Crayons in All" (from Session 4.4), and "Total of Six" (from Session 4.5)
SESSION FOLLOW-UP **③** **Practice**		• *Student Math Handbook Flip Chart,* pp. 28, 29

Classroom Routines

Today's Question: Do you like to play sports? On chart paper, create a horizontal table titled "Do you like to play sports?" with "Yes" written at the left of one row and "No" written at the left of the other row. Students respond by writing their names on stick-on notes and sticking them in the appropriate row. Count the responses as a class and discuss what the results of the survey tell you.

Teaching Note

❶ Students Who Do Not Yet Meet the Benchmark
As you do the End-of-Unit Assessment interviews, you may come across a few students who do not yet meet one or more of the benchmarks for this unit. Watch closely as these students complete the assessment tasks in order to figure out as specifically as you can what it is these students are struggling with. For example, does the student need more practice with the names of the numbers? The sequence? Does she or he need to figure out a system for organizing and keeping track of a count? Is she or he not sure that the last number she or he says represents the number of objects in the group? With such specific information, you can plan next steps—from meeting with them one-on-one to working with a small group, to assigning particular activities during Math Workshop—that match students' needs. Also, know that students will get more practice with counting, combining, and using numbers to represent quantities in the remaining unit, *Sorting and Surveys*.

MATH WORKSHOP

① Combinations and Assessments

20–35 MIN

Explain that three activities are available during Math Workshop.

- *Total of Six,* See Session 4.3, pages 147–149
- *Toss the Chips,* See Session 1.2, page 36
- *Racing Bears,* See Session 1.5, pages 51–53

Remind students what each activity entails, what materials are required, and where they are located. Explain that, while students are at work on these activities, you will be meeting individually with students.

While students are working on these activities, meet individually with those you need to assess. (See Session 4.5, pages 157–158.)❶

DISCUSSION

② Combinations of Six

10 MIN   CLASS

Math Focus Points for Discussion

◆ Considering combinations of a number (e.g. 6 is 3 and 3 and also 5 and 1)

Post the chart paper posters you made for *Toss the Chips* with 6 chips (from Session 4.2), Six Crayons in All (from Session 4.4), and *Total of Six* (from Session 4.5) so that students can see them.

Here are the posters we made for Toss the Chips, *Six Crayons in All, and* Total of Six. *Take a minute to look them over carefully. What do you notice?*

Some students notice what is different about them. For example, the *Toss the Chips* paper uses a table, the Six Crayons in All poster uses pictures, and the *Total of Six* poster has equations. For some students, such differences mask any similarities. Others are able to see that the same numbers and/or combinations appear on some or all of the sheets.

[Beth] said that they all *show 3 and 3. [Beth], can you show us where you see 3 and 3 on the* Toss the Chips *chart? [Jae], can you find the 3 and 3 [Beth] saw on our Six Crayons in All poster? What about the* Total of Six *poster?*

Although many students will pick out a given combination, most will not be able to articulate why it appears on every poster. You can challenge them to think about this question by asking the following:

Are you surprised that [Beth] found the same numbers, or combinations, on all three posters? Why or why not? What if I asked you to look at our posters to find the combination 4 and 2?

Students' explanations are likely to rely on the fact that all three activities focused on the number 6. Some may be able to reason further, that the activities involve splitting six into two (or more, for *Total of Six*) parts. In other words, each activity asked students to find combinations of 6. Because the problem is the same, the answers should be the same. ❷

You might end by asking students the challenging question of whether a combination of 5 or 7 should appear on any of your posters.

What if I asked you to look at our posters to find the combination of 3 and 2? Would you find 3 and 2 on one of our posters? Why or why not?

SESSION FOLLOW-UP

 3 Practice

Student Math Handbook Flip Chart: Use the *Student Math Handbook Flip Chart* pages 28, 29 to reinforce concepts from today's session. See pages 189–193 in the back of this unit.

Algebra Note

❷ **3 and 3 Is 6 No Matter What** As students recognize the same numerical relationships across contexts, that $3 + 3 = 6$ whether you are talking about red and yellow chips, red and blue crayons, or Primary Number Cards, they are building a foundation for understanding the operation of addition.

Professional Development

UNIT 6

How Many Do You Have?

In Part 6 of *Implementing Investigations in Kindergarten,* you will find a set of Teacher Notes that addresses topics and issues applicable to the curriculum as a whole rather than to specific curriculum units. They include the following:

Computational Fluency and Place Value

Computation Algorithms and Methods

Representations and Contexts for Mathematical Work

Foundations of Algebra in the Elementary Grades

Discussing Mathematical Ideas

Racial and Linguistic Diversity in the Classroom: Raising Questions About What Equity in the Math Classroom Means Today

Introducing Notation in Kindergarten

Kindergarteners need many opportunities to develop their own ways of recording their mathematical work. It is important to keep the emphasis on ways of recording that come from the students, rather than from the teacher. However, it is not too early to begin exposing students to a variety of ways of recording, including equations when appropriate. Keep in mind that, although a few kindergarteners may begin incorporating equations, most will probably not be ready to use equations in a meaningful way for another year or two. Although the equation format may seem very straightforward to adults, it actually assumes some complex ideas about number relationships. To use an equation meaningfully, students need to understand the quantities, operations, and relationships that it shows. In the early primary grades, students are just beginning to develop these understandings as they work on counting and number combinations.

Use equations only when they naturally describe the numerical approaches that students themselves are using. For example, for a problem that involves combining 2 and 2 and 2, a student might say, "I knew that 2 and 2 is 4, and then I added the 2 more, and 4 and 2 is 6." This is a perfect opportunity to record with equations:

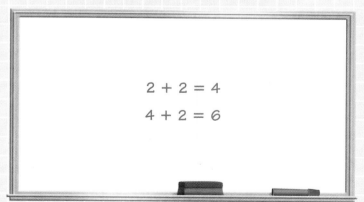

Another student might use both number combinations and counting for the same problem: "I knew that 2 and 2

is 4, and then I did 2 more, and that's 5, 6." In this case, you could record in a way that reflects both approaches:

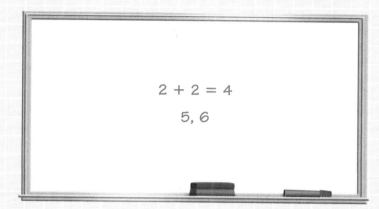

Yet another student might count to solve the same problem, putting up a finger for each number while saying: "2 and 2 and 2, that's 1, 2, then 3, 4, and then 5, 6." This student's method suggests recording in some way other than the equation format, for example:

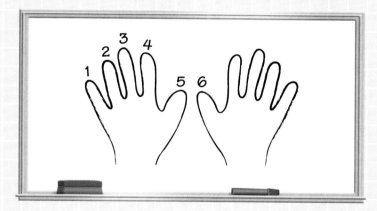

Do your best to match your way of recording to what the students say, in order to share and give credit to a variety of ways of thinking about and recording the problem. The focus in Kindergarten is on having students develop clear ways of thinking about and understanding the action of a problem. In first grade, students will develop these ideas further and will focus on how they can use symbols and notation to represent both the action in a problem and their problem-solving strategies. In addition, they will work from symbols and notation, telling stories that match a given equation, such as $7 + 3 = $ _____ or $10 - 3 = $ _____.

Expect students who are just beginning to use equations to use them incorrectly. For example, you may see students who, for $3 + 3 = 6$, record:

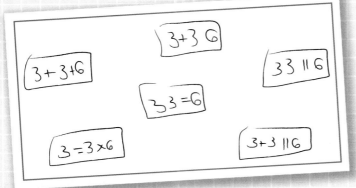

Sample Student Work

When asked to describe their work, many of these students say that what they have written shows that "3 plus 3 equals 6." Developing an understanding of how to use such notation requires several things. Students need to know what the symbols mean and which symbols stand for which action (+) or relationship (=), and they need many opportunities to use and see others, including their teacher, use it. But, more importantly, it requires an understanding of the operation of addition.

Over the course of Grades K–2, students have many experiences with the operation of addition. Initially grounded in counting activities, students gradually come to understand that one way to view counting is as a process that involves adding one more. Students also make sense of the action of addition—it is about combining or joining groups and then finding the total. With an understanding of such ideas, students become ready to think about and use standard notation with meaning—to represent what they understand about the quantities (3, 3, and 6), actions (+), and relationships (=) in a problem. Expect their fluency with notation to develop as their understanding of the operation deepens, as they and their classmates experiment with it, and as they see it modeled by you.

Observing Kindergarteners as They Count

In Kindergarten, you can expect to see a wide range of number skills within your class. Students in the same class can vary considerably in age and in their previous experience with numbers and counting.

Your students will have many opportunities to count and use numbers not only in this unit, but throughout the year. You can learn a great deal about what your students understand by observing them. Listen to students as they talk with one another. Observe them as they count orally, as they count objects, and as they use numerals to record. Ask them about their thinking. You may observe some of the following:

Counting Orally

By the end of the year, most kindergarteners will have learned to rote count to 10 and beyond, with some able to count as high as 100. Many will be able to count orally much higher than they can count objects. Many who have learned the internal counting pattern or sequence (1, 2, 3 . . . 21, 22, 23 . . .), will still find the "bridge" numbers into the next decade (such as 19, 20, or 29, 30) difficult. You may hear children count "twenty-eight, twenty-nine, twenty-ten." Just as the young child who says "I runned away" understands something about the regularities of the English language, the student who says "twenty-ten" understands something about the regularity of the counting numbers. Students gradually learn the bridge numbers as they hear and use the counting sequence.

Counting Quantities

Most kindergarteners end the year with a grasp of *quantities* up to 20 or so. Some students accurately count quantities above 20, while others may not consistently count smaller quantities. Some may be inconsistent and count successfully one time while having difficulty the next.

Even when students can accurately count the objects in a set, they may not know that the last number counted also describes the number of objects in the set. You may observe students who successfully count a set of cubes, but have to go back and recount the set to answer the question, "How many cubes are there?" These students have not yet connected the counting numbers to the quantity of objects in a set. Students develop their understanding of quantity through repeated experiences organizing and counting sets of objects. In Kindergarten, many of the activities that focus on quantity can be adjusted so that students are working at a level of challenge appropriate for them.

Organizing a Count

Some students may be able to count objects they can pick up, move around, and organize with far more accuracy than they can when counting static objects, such as pictures of things on a page. You may observe some students who can count objects correctly when the group is organized for them, but you will see others who have trouble organizing or keeping track of objects themselves. They will need many and varied experiences with counting to develop techniques for counting accurately and for keeping track of what they are counting.

Counting by Writing Numbers

Knowing how to write numerals is not directly related to counting and understanding quantity; however, it is useful for representing a quantity that has been counted. Young students who are learning how to write numerals frequently reverse numbers or digits. Often this is not a mathematical problem but a matter of experience. Students need many opportunities to see how numerals are formed and to practice writing them. They should gain this experience by using numbers to record mathematical information, such as the number of students in school today or the number of objects on a page of a counting book. Numeral formation is related to letter formation; both are important in order to communicate in writing. We recommend that rote practice of numeral writing be part of handwriting instruction rather than mathematics.

Counting Is More Than 1, 2, 3

Counting is the basis for understanding our number system and for almost all of the number work in the primary grades. It involves more than just knowing the number names, their sequence, and how to write each number. While it may seem simple, counting is actually quite complex and involves the interplay between a number of skills and concepts.

Rote Counting

Students need to know the number names and their order by rote; they learn this sequence—both forward and backward—by hearing others count and by counting themselves. However, just as saying the alphabet does not indicate that a student can use written language, being able to say "one, two, three, four, five, six, seven, eight, nine, ten" does not necessarily indicate that students know what those counting words mean. Students also need to use numbers in meaningful ways if they are to build an understanding of quantity and number relationships.

One-to-One Correspondence

To count accurately, a student must know that one number name stands for one object that is being counted. Often, when young children first begin to count, they do not connect the numbers in the "counting song" to the objects they are counting. Children learn about one-to-one correspondence through repeated opportunities to count sets of objects and to watch others as they count. One-to-one correspondence develops over time with students first counting small groups of objects (up to five or six) accurately, and eventually larger groups.

Keeping Track

Another important part of counting accurately is being able to keep track of what has already been counted and what remains to be counted. As students first learn to count sets of objects, they often count some objects more than once and skip other objects altogether. Students develop strategies for organizing and keeping track of a count as they realize the need and as they see others use such strategies.

Connecting Numbers to Quantities

Many young students are still coordinating the ordinal sequence of the numbers with the cardinal meaning of those numbers. In other words, we get to 5 by counting in order 1, 2, 3, 4, 5. Understanding this aspect of number is connected to the one-to-one correspondence between the numbers we say and the objects we are counting. However, being able to count accurately using this ordinal sequence is not the same as knowing that when we have finished counting, the final number in our sequence will tell us the quantity of the things we have counted.

Conservation

Conservation of number involves understanding that three is always three, whether it is three objects together, three objects spread apart, or some other formation. As students learn to count, you will see many who do not yet understand this idea. They think that the larger the arrangement of objects, the more objects there are. Being able to conserve quantity is not a skill that can be taught; it is a cognitive process that develops as children grow.

Counting by Groups

Counting a set of objects by equal groups such as 2s, requires that each of the steps mentioned above happens again, at a different level. Students need to know the 2s sequence (2, 4, 6, 8) by rote. They need to realize that one number in this count represents two objects, and that each time they say a number they are adding another group of two to their count. Keeping track while counting by groups becomes a more complex task as well. Students begin to explore counting by groups in Session 1.3, How Many Eyes? as they count the number of eyes in their class. However, most students will not count by groups in a meaningful way until first or second grade.

Learning About Length: Lining Up Units

In Kindergarten, students start working with ideas about what is *long, longer, short,* and *shorter*. Their ideas begin to develop as they compare lengths directly.

"My sister is taller than I am."

"My pencil is the shortest in the class."

Research on children's mathematical understanding shows that students typically do not develop a firm idea about length as a stable, measurable dimension until second grade, although there is quite a range of individual differences among students. Through many experiences with measuring and comparing, students develop their understanding of what length is and how it can be described.

Students in your class may vary quite a bit in how accurately and consistently they measure the lengths of things. Some do not carefully line up their sticks or cubes end to end when they use them to measure, instead either overlapping the units or leaving spaces between them. Others measure with a single object (such as a craft stick) by running it along a given length as they count "1, 2, 3, 4, . . ." without paying much attention to whether each successive placement begins where the previous one ended. These *mistakes* are probably not just carelessness or sloppiness; instead, these students are still figuring out what measuring is about.

Rather than simply tell students to carefully line up sticks along a length of tape, encourage discussion among students about the different ways they are measuring:

Some people said that this shelf was eight sticks long, some said nine, and some said eleven. Who would like to show how you measured this shelf? . . . Raul lined up eight sticks like this. Do you think that's all right? Could it be nine sticks? Could that work? Why or why not?

At times, you may show students some inaccurate ways of measuring to help them think through and articulate their own ideas. For example, spread out three sticks, with big gaps along the edge of the shelf—one at the beginning of the shelf, one in the middle, and one lined up with the far end. Tell students that you measured this shelf and found that it was three sticks long. Ask them whether that is correct and, if not, what you should do to get a better measurement. As students discuss and compare ways of measuring, they will gradually grasp what length is and how to measure it accurately.

Students need to have many experiences with units that they can place repeatedly along a length and count (such as craft sticks, cubes, or their feet) so that they physically experience what length is, how it extends from one point to another, and how two lengths can be compared.

Because many students have seen people using rulers or yardsticks to measure objects, they may be interested in using such tools. You can make rulers available, but in the early grades, students usually see the numbers on a ruler simply as marks to read without understanding just how a ruler is used to quantify length. For example, some students align the end of an object with the 1, rather than with the end of the ruler. Others use the ruler backward, reporting a length of ten inches when it is actually two.

Students sometimes think that one measuring unit is equivalent to another; for example, they will find that an object is six cubes long and report the length as six inches. They may also think that when one object is longer than another, it must be one more unit long. For example, a 7-year-old who was four feet tall compared herself with a classmate. He was a few inches taller, so she said, "So he's five feet tall."

As students' understanding of measurement develops in Grades K–1, they begin to formulate ideas about the need for standard units of measure. The understanding they develop through many experiences of using nonstandard units will become the basis for understanding the use of standard measuring tools. The need for a standard measuring tool is among the topics students investigate in Grade 2 Measuring Length and Time.

Assessing Addition

By the end of this unit, students are expected to be able to combine two small quantities (Benchmark 3). This means that they can solve an addition problem with small numbers, whether presented through a story problem, a roll of two dot cubes, or a round of *Double Compare*. They may count all, count on, just know some combinations, or use combinations they know to figure out ones they do not know. Assessment Checklist: Addition (M12) is included to help you keep track of your observations about students' strategies over the course of this Investigation and unit. What follows is a vignette from one teacher, describing what she learned about students as she observed their work during Investigations 2 and 3.

After investigating Inventory Bags that contained sets of related objects—five pencils, four markers, and five crayons, for example—I was curious to see what students would do when I put 10 square tiles in the Counting Jar, 5 red and 5 blue.

Mary and Latoya dumped the tiles out and made two lines, one with 5 red, the other with 5 blue. Mary counted them by 1s, but Latoya said, "I don't need to count. This is 5 and this is 5 and 5 and 5 is 10." I asked, "How do you know that 5 and 5 is 10?" She put both hands up in the air, saying "5" as she waved one and then "5" as she waved the other, "that's 10."

As usual, Jack worked methodically. He used his preferred strategy—taking the tiles out of the jar one at a time, and counting them as he did so—making the subsets irrelevant. I asked what he found out and he told me, "10." I asked whether he noticed anything about the tiles. "There are 10." I asked how many were red and how many were blue. He sorted the tiles, counted each group, and announced that there were 5. I said, "So there are 5 red tiles and 5 blue tiles. How many tiles are there altogether?" He counted the tiles from 1 and told me, "10."

Emma arranged the tiles in groups of 2, each with one red and one blue. "I made a pattern." I asked, "Does your pattern help you know how many tiles there are?" Emma thought for a second, pointed at two of the groups of 2, and then said excitedly, "2 and 2 is 4! . . . And . . . [she paused and then pointed at the other groups of 2] 2 and 2 and 2." I asked,

"So how many tiles do you have altogether?" Stumped about how to connect her groups of 2 to a total, she went silent. I moved the two groups of 2 she initially pointed out, separating them a bit from the rest, and said, "You said that 2 and 2 is 4 . . ." Emma: Right. That's 4 . . . [touching each remaining tile] 5, 6, 7, 8, 9, 10.

Roll and Record 3 gave me lots of opportunities to watch students combine small amounts. (I also quickly got a sense of who still had to count to see what number they had rolled, and how children were doing with the written numbers to ten.)

Mitchell and Jason rolled a 6 and a 1. Mitchell immediately announced, "7. Again!" (They had already rolled 7 several times, and he sounded somewhat amazed to have rolled another one.) When I asked how he knew so quickly he said, "After 6 is 7." I wondered if Jason was "with" us—Mitchell instantly "saw" the problem (6 + 1), solved it quickly, and his explanation did not explicitly state the problem he had solved. I rephrased, pointing to each dot cube: "So Mitchell said that 6 and 1 more is 7, because when we count we say 6, 7." Then I asked Jason to roll the dot cubes and show me how he figures out what number to write. He rolled double 2s and said excitedly, "I know that one! 2 and 2 is 4." He put up 2 fingers on either hand and then touched each finger to his chin to show me that it was, in fact, 4. I watched a few more turns. Mitchell clearly knows the dot patterns and, if he does not know the combination, he counts on. Jason knew some of the doubles and seemed to count on when one of the cubes showed 1 or 2. Other times he counted from one, but did so with accuracy.

The story problems in this Investigation also gave me a lot of information about how students are making sense of addition situations. Although recording their work was a challenge for many, I was pleased that almost all of my students seemed to understand addition as combining or joining groups. Most counted all to find the total, but some are consistently counting on, others are fluent with some combinations (particularly the doubles and ones that involve adding one or two) and some even use the combinations they know to solve another ("I know 3 and 3 is 6, so 3 and 4 is 7").

To solve a story problem I posed about 6 and 2 more, Abby counted on on her fingers: "7, 8." I asked Manuel, who had counted out 6 buttons and then 2 more, if he agreed. Thinking he would count the buttons, I was surprised when Manuel said, "She's right because look, you can see 4 plus 4."

Given that Rebecca and Corey were working on recording their work for a story problem (about Yoshio finding 3 balls and then 2 more) when I joined them, I was surprised when Corey said, "I don't know yet" when I asked how many balls Yoshio had found. "First I drew 3. Now I'm drawing the other 2. Then I'm going to count them." At that point, Rebecca, who had written "5" on her paper, announced: "It's easy. It's 5 because 2 plus 2 is 4. I know that one by heart." "But Rebecca," I asked, "You are talking about 2 plus 2 and didn't Yoshio find 3 balls and 2 balls?" Rebecca replied, "Yeah but 2 plus 2 is in 3 plus 2." I asked what she meant by 2 + 2 being in 3 + 2. She pointed to Corey's drawing. "Look 2 plus 2. [She used 4 fingers, 2 from each hand, to cover 4 of Corey's pictures of balls.] And then there's 1 more. 5!" I acknowledged that Rebecca used something she knew and decided to challenge her: "When I look at your paper, I see that there are 5 balls at the end of the story. I'm wondering whether there's anything you could add that would show how you thought about the problem?" When I looked through the pile of completed work later that day, Rebecca had added "2 + 2 = 4" to her paper.

Assessment Checklist: Addition ✓

Student	Notes
Mary	Count by 1s
Latoya	C. - Jar - line of 5 red 5 blue "5 and 5 is 10" 👆 👆
Jack	C. - Jar - counts as removes - 10 ?: how many blue? (counts 5) red? (counts 5) how many altogether? counts 1 – 10
Emma	C. - Jar 1R 1B 1R 1B 1R 1B "I made a pattern" 2 and 2 is 4! . . . and 2 and 2 and 2. . . . 4; 5 6 7 8 9 10.
Mitchell	R + R: (6 + 1) 7! Again! just knows "after 6 is 7" or counts on
Jason	R + R: (2 + 2) I know that one! Knows it, 1 + 1, 2 + 2, 3 + 3. Counts on if a 1 or (sometimes) a 2
Abby	Story prob—6 + 2—counts on on fingers
Manuel	counts out buttons but hears "8" from Abby & "sees" 4 + 4 in his buttons.
Rebecca	it's easy - 5 . . . b/c 2 + 2 is 4 ⊠ ⊠ ○ . . . 2 + 2 is in 3 + 2. Shows me ⊠ ⊠ story prob on Corey's drawing
Corey	3 + 2 draws 3 draws 2 counts f — 1

In order to accurately add small amounts, students need to have an understanding of the operation of addition. Whether they count all, count on, just know a combination, or use a combination they know to figure out a combination they do not know, students need to be able to visualize the combining or joining action that characterizes the operation of addition. Therefore, students spend time retelling and acting out story problems and modeling the action of them with cubes, whether or not they use such strategies to actually solve the problem. This work builds a foundation that supports students as they solve problems and work on combining games and activities (e.g., *Roll and Record 3, Double Compare,* Counting Jar, Inventory Bags).

Creating Your Own Story Problems

Following are story problems you can use as you repeat the activity, Acting Out Story Problems, over the course of this unit.

Story Problems That Involve Combining

- Seven children were splashing in the swimming pool. Two more children got into the swimming pool, and they all splashed around together. (Then how many children were splashing in the swimming pool?)

- Eight birds were sitting on a tree branch, flapping their wings. Two more birds flew over to join them. (Then how many birds were on the tree branch?)

- Six children were jumping rope on the playground. Five more came and joined them. (Then how many children were jumping rope on the playground?)

- Heather had six toy cars. Noah gave her two more toy cars. (How many toy cars does Heather have now?)

- Santos had five shells. He found four more shells. (Now how many shells does Santos have?)

- On Monday, Clara took five books out of the library. On Tuesday, she took five more books out of the library. (How many books did Clara take out of the library in all?)

Story Problems That Involve Separating

- Eight children were digging in the sandbox. Three of the children went over to the swings. (How many children were left digging in the sandbox?)

- Eight snakes were slithering around in the grass. Four of the snakes slithered into a hole to sleep. (How many snakes were still slithering around in the grass?)

- Ten cats were sleeping on the kitchen floor. Two of the cats woke up and went outside. (How many cats were left sleeping on the kitchen floor?)

- Ginny had six grapes. She ate three of them. (Now how many grapes does she have?)

- Ahmad had five flowers. He gave four of them to Krista. (How many flowers did he have left?)

- Seven apples were hanging from a branch of an apple tree. Taniqua picked three of them. (How many apples were left on the branch of the tree?)

Many teachers prefer to create their own problems. This enables them to use story contexts that reflect the interests, knowledge, and environment of their own students, as well as to adjust the numbers appropriately.

Creating Interesting Contexts

In creating, combining, and separating situations, use contexts that are familiar and interesting to students without being distracting. For example, you can change a problem about a class trip to a fire station to reflect a trip to a familiar place in your community. Teachers find that simple situations that are familiar to all their students are the most satisfying. One source of good situations is experiences that you know all your students have had. For example, one class walks to a nearby park every day for recess; a problem based on that experience might be:

When we were at the park today, I counted three birds on the ground and four more in a tree. How many birds did I see in the park?

Another class is taking a field trip:

We have two teachers and four parents coming with us on our field trip today. How many grown-ups are coming with us?

Sometimes teachers present stories about their students, being sure to use the name of each child in a story at some point. You can also make up two characters who have experiences very much like those of your students. Give them names or let the students name them, and build all of your problem situations around these characters.

Jana and Skye were drawing a big picture of rockets. Jana drew four rockets and Skye drew two rockets. How many rockets did they draw?

Jana and Skye went to the toy store. Jana bought four stickers and Skye bought two stickers. How many stickers did they buy?

Students seem to enjoy the consistency and familiarity of recurring characters.

You can also take advantage of special events, classroom happenings, seasons, or holidays for problem contexts.

If Jana made two snowballs and Skye made five, how many snowballs did they have?

Related Problems

Simple, familiar situations often suggest other problems that easily follow from the initial one. Such follow-up questions can be posed on the spot to students who need more challenge. Additional problems related to the previous examples might include the following:

Yesterday at the park, I counted six birds on the ground and two in the trees. Did I see more birds or fewer birds than I saw today?

Jana and Skye drew four more rockets. Now how many rockets are in their picture?

Jana and Skye gave away three of their stickers. How many did they have left?

Jana and Skye made four more snowballs. Then how many did they have?

Adjusting Numbers in the Problem

You will probably see wide variation in the numbers with which your students are comfortable working. Try to present problems at a medium level of challenge for most students. For problems that involve combining, totals from six up to ten or twelve are at the right level for many kindergarteners. Problems that involve separating are usually more difficult

for young students, so start with slightly smaller numbers—initial amounts up to seven or eight, with amounts of two, three, or four to be removed.

The problems in this unit follow these guidelines, but you may feel that these numbers are not appropriate for your students. Keep in mind that in this unit, students have experience with numbers in the teens and higher as they play these games *Double Compare, Collect 15 Together,* and their variations. The numbers in the story problems are deliberately small so that students can focus on making sense of the story, choosing appropriate solution strategies, and communicating these strategies in a way that others can understand. Although at times you may want to challenge students by giving them problems with larger numbers, you can also challenge them by asking them to find answers in more than one way and to find ways to explain their solution strategies more clearly.

Important Note on Problem Structure

In Kindergarten, students work with two familiar and simple problem structures: combining two amounts to find a total and removing one amount from another to find how much is left. There are many other story problem structures, varying widely in level of difficulty. When you change the context or numbers in a problem, be sure not to change the structure of the problem because this can significantly alter its level of difficulty. For example, this problem is at an appropriate level for many Kindergarten students:

I had six apples. I gave two apples to my sister. How many do I have left?

However, a change in problem structure can yield a much more difficult problem.

I have six apples. My sister has two apples. How many more apples do I have?

This second problem is likely to be too challenging for many kindergarteners.

Story Problems in Kindergarten

Presenting Story Problems

In order to solve story problems, young students first need to be able to think about the sequence of actions in the story. This is why much of the work with story problems in Kindergarten involves children picturing the story in their minds, retelling the story in their own words, and actually acting out the action of the story. Some teachers encourage students to close their eyes to help them concentrate, and others draw quick sketches of important words on the board to help students understand and imagine the story.

The goal of this work is to help students think about the actions in the stories and choose strategies that reflect those actions, rather than choose strategies because they have been told that the problem is of a certain type. By *not* telling students whether a story is about joining or taking away and not presenting it in a predictable sequence (e.g., always combining followed by separating), students must concentrate on the actions in the story to figure out how to solve it.

We suggest that teachers use words such as *combining* and *separating* in addition to words like *adding* and *subtracting*, because they emphasize the actions involved in the stories. These terms also take into account that students may solve problems in a variety of ways. For example, they may solve *separating* problems using strategies based on either subtraction (or counting back) or addition (or counting on).

We caution against overuse of the expression "take away" for subtraction. Although "take away" is one way to conceptualize a subtraction problem (and the only way it is presented in Kindergarten), students will encounter others types of situations in Grades 1 and 2 that are also modeled by subtraction equations. For example, the following are all possible story problems for $7 - 2 = 5$:

- I had 7, and Karen took away 2. Now how many do I have?

- I have 7 and Karen has 2. How many more do I have? (Or, how many fewer does Karen have?)

- I have 2 (or 5). How many more do I need to get to 7?

- How far is it from 2 to 7? (Or, what is the distance between 2 and 7?)

- I had 7. I lost some. Now I have 5. How many did I lose?

Sharing Strategies

There are always some students who are eager just to give an answer; teachers are encouraged to keep the emphasis on the solution strategies children use. In Kindergarten, you are likely to see a wide range:

For addition stories, some students will suggest counting out each group of people or objects in a story, and then counting them all, from one. Others will do the same thing, but use their fingers. Some will be ready to think about counting on, with objects, on their fingers, or in their heads. ("If there were 4, and then 3 more came, that's 5, 6, 7.") Some children might "just know" that 3 and 4 is 7, and a few will use combinations that they "just know" to solve other related problems; for example, "I know that 3 and 3 is 6, and 1 more makes 7."

Strategies you are likely to see for subtraction story problems include counting out the total number, removing some, and counting the number of objects remaining, or a similar but less typical strategy of counting back. Although some Kindergarten students may "just know" some addition combinations, they are less likely to be familiar with subtraction facts. However, they may use their knowledge of addition combinations to solve such a problem: "I know 2 and 5 make 7. You had 7 and dropped 2, so there has to be 5 left."

Discussions About the Operation

Another part of the story problem routine involves questions about the operations. Thinking about how stories are the same or different help students focus on what is special about the operations of addition and subtraction. Some students focus on how the quantities change: when you add you end up with more; subtraction situations leave you with less than the original number. In the words of a five- or six-year-old "[For combining stories] you get a bigger number than you started with." If you have [6] and you take some away, you will have less than [6]. Other students talk more about the actions in the stories. In one kind of story, 2 (or more) groups are put together, joined, or combined; the other type of story involves part of a group being taken away, separated, or lost.

Understand that it may be challenging for some kindergarteners to reason in this way. Over the next couple of years, as they solve a wide variety of story problems, they will gain an understanding of what kinds of actions suggest combining and what kinds suggest separating. They will also learn to consider relationships among the quantities in a story. This kind of thinking will enable them to tackle problems that involve larger numbers and more complex structures—problems that they may not be able to act out easily.

Three Approaches to Story Problems in Kindergarten

Students commonly take one of three approaches to solving story problems about combining: counting all, counting on (or up), and numerical reasoning. Each approach is described below.

Yoshio was in charge of cleaning up after recess. He found 3 balls by the swings. Then he found 2 more by the slide. How many balls did Yoshio find?

Counting All

When young students first encounter story problem situations, they usually model the actions in the problem step-by-step in order to solve it. For example, to solve the problem above, these students count out or draw a group of 3, a group of 2, and then count all of the objects or pictures from one.

As students gain skill in visualizing problem situations and begin to develop a repertoire of number relationships they know, they gradually develop other strategies based on counting on and numerical reasoning. These strategies require visualizing all of the quantities of the problem and their relationships, and recognizing which quantities you know and which you need to find.

Counting On

Other students use strategies that involve counting on. These students count on from 3 (or from 2) to solve the above problem. For example:

Brad lays out a group of 3 cubes and a group of 2 cubes. He covers the group of 3 cubes with one hand and says, "That's 3." Then he touches the other 2 cubes, one at a time, saying, "4, 5."

Emma: Well, there's 2 and there's 3. So 2 and then [raises three fingers] 3, 4, 5 [she wiggles one finger for each number].

Lionel: 3 plus 2 is 3, 4, 5.

The difference between this strategy and counting all can be quite subtle. For example, Brad directly models the problem, much like students who count all. However, when Brad finds the total number of cubes, he does not count the group of 3 from 1. Instead, he can see and trust it as "3" and can hold that quantity in his head while he operates on the group of 2, counting "4, 5." Emma represents only the group of 3 with her fingers, and Lionel does not explicitly represent either group. Both children have visual images that enable them to successfully represent the groups, and the action of the problem, mentally. Note that this strategy also involves double counting, which can be quite complicated for young students. For example, consider Emma's strategy. She raises three fingers (1, 2, 3), but counts them as 4, 5, and 6.

Using Numerical Reasoning

As students learn some number combinations and more about number relationships, they begin to be able to use what they know to solve problems. For example, consider how Russell solved $6 + 4$ while playing *Double Compare*:

Russell: If I take a 1 from the 6 [and give it to the 4], it makes two 5s and that's 10.

Or, listen to Rebecca's reasoning as she solves the problem about three and two:

Rebecca: That's easy. It's 5 because 2 plus 2 is 4. I know that one by heart. [When questioned, she explains further.] 2 plus 2 is in 3 plus 2. [She points to her neighbor's drawing, of 3 balls and 2 balls.] Look. 2 plus 2. [She uses two fingers from each hand to cover four of the pictures of balls.] And then there's 1 more. 5!

These students do not count by 1s; in fact, they do not count at all. Both can see the problem as a whole and identify number relationships that they know to help them solve the problem. Russell turns $6 + 4$ into $5 + 5$, a problem he knows, by taking 1 from the 6 and giving it to the 4 (e.g., $6 + 4 = 5 + 5$). Rebecca knows that 3 can be broken into a 2 and a 1, which enables her to think of the problem as $2 + 2$, which she knows by heart, and 1 more (e.g., $2 + 3 = 2 + 2 + 1$).

Note that the strategies kindergarteners use to solve story problems about removing or separating are quite similar to the ones described above. Most students directly model subtraction problems—they show all of the objects involved, cross or separate out the ones that are removed, and count the ones that remain. Some students count back to solve such problems and a few may use an addition or a subtraction fact they know.

Although it is important to encourage counting on strategies and strategies that use numerical reasoning, keep in mind that the ability to work with groups of more than 1 develops gradually over the early elementary years. Most kindergarteners need to count by 1s for most problems. As they build their understanding of number combinations and number relationships over the next year or two, as well as their ability to visualize the structure of a problem as a whole, they will begin developing more flexible strategies.

Double Compare: Strategies for Combining and Comparing

Through the game of *Double Compare*, students develop strategies for combining two numbers and for reasoning about quantity. The following scenes from a classroom illustrate situations that commonly arise and show how to adjust the game for students at different levels.

Counting Objects

Students develop strategies for adding by drawing cards and combining the numbers on the cards.

As Jae turns up a 3 and a 0 and Sarah turns up two 8 cards, Jae begins by reminding himself, "Count those little things [the pictures on the cards]." Then, while Sarah watches, he counts each picture on the 3 card, touching them as he says the numbers. He announces that he has 3.

Sarah places her cards side by side, overlapping the edges. She counts slowly, touching all of the pictures as she says the numbers. However, she skips a few pictures, counts a few twice, and comes up with a total of 13. Jae says that he thinks 8 and 8 is 18. Although they are aware that at least one of these totals is inaccurate, they realize that regardless, Sarah's total is greater than Jae's total of 3, and they are ready to move on.

At this point the teacher steps in and asks them to recount Sarah's total, slowly. After a couple of trials, Sarah and Jae both come up with a total of 16. The teacher suggests that they use interlocking cubes to help them find the totals on their cards. Because cubes, unlike the pictures on the cards, can be moved around, they can make it easier for students to keep track of what they have counted and what they have left to count.

Sarah and Jae both need to count by ones to be sure of their totals, and counting totals greater than 10 is challenging for them. The teacher plans to return in a few minutes to see whether the cubes are helpful. If Sarah and Jae are still having difficulty working with larger numbers, she will suggest that they play with only the 1–6 cards. Later in the session, she will call together students having difficulty and will work with them as they play *Double Compare*.

Counting and Counting On

Manuel's cards   Dennis's cards

Manuel and Dennis get right to work finding their totals. Dennis counts quietly to himself. He begins at 9, and then counts "10, 11, 12, 13, 14." With each number he says, Dennis uses his right index finger to bend back one of the fingers on his left hand. When he has bent back all of the fingers on his left hand, he stops counting and announces that he has 14.

Meanwhile, Manuel is still counting. He began by looking first at the 7 card and counting from one to seven. Then, he turned to the 4 card and began counting "8, 9, . . ." When Dennis announced his total of 14, Manuel lost his place. He begins counting again. He counts to seven, and then he counts the pictures on the 4 card, saying "8" as he points to the first picture, "9" as he points to the second, and so on, until he reaches 11. The boys agree that Dennis has the greater total. Like Sarah, Manuel puts the two quantities together and counts them all, starting at one. Dennis can begin with one quantity and count on, starting with the next number. In order to do this, Dennis treats nine as a unit; that is, he can think of it as nine without breaking it down into ones again. Then, he counts on—"10, 11, 12, 13, 14"—while keeping track with his fingers of how many he needs to add (1, 2, 3, 4, 5). The teacher believes that the game is at an appropriate level of challenge for Dennis and Manuel. In future sessions, she will observe them to see how their strategies for counting and combining are developing. For example, she will note whether Manuel continues counting from one each time and whether they have begun developing strategies for determining particular combinations without counting.

"Just Knowing" Number Combinations

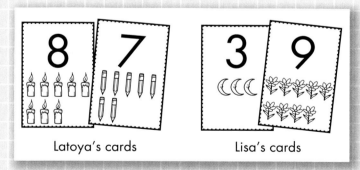

Latoya's cards   Lisa's cards

As Latoya and Lisa turn over their cards, Latoya immediately announces that she has 15, and then looks over at Lisa's cards. The teacher reminds Latoya to let Lisa find her own total. Meanwhile, Lisa counts almost inaudibly to herself "10, 11, 12," and then says that her total is 12. Latoya says, "Me! I won."

How did you get your totals?

Latoya: Because I know eight and seven make 15. Because it's easy.

On the next round, Latoya again immediately announces her total, and then waits impatiently while Lisa slowly counts on from nine.

When the teacher again asks how the girls found their solutions, Latoya is still unable to explain. She seems either to have memorized some number combinations or to have developed strategies for finding solutions to number combinations quickly. Latoya is eager to play at a faster pace than she can with Lisa, so the teacher decides to ask her to play with Russell, who is also finding number combinations quickly. To provide further challenge, she may ask Latoya and Russell to turn over three cards on a round.

Reasoning About Number Combinations

Jason's cards   Mia's cards

Jason: 1 and 5 is 6. I have 6.

Mia: 8, 9, . . . [*after a short pause*] Me! Because you have 6 and I have more.

Jason's cards   Mia's cards

Jason: Me! 9 is bigger than 0. You know because it's just your eyes that tell you.

Mia and Jason are reasoning about the number pairs without necessarily needing to add them up. Although the teacher has observed in previous sessions that Jason and Mia are skilled at counting, combining, and comparing numbers, she believes that this game is deepening their understanding of numbers and number relationships as they explore ways to reason about numbers.

Choosing a Card to Win a Round

Carmen's cards   Kiyo's cards

Carmen and Kiyo count together slowly, starting with Carmen's cards. Carmen touches the pictures as she counts. Kiyo tells her that she has counted a picture twice, and they begin again. After several trials, they complete the count with a total of 12.

Kiyo: 6 and 1 is 7. But it's my turn to win this time . . . [She places her cards side by side so that the one is to the left of the six.] It's 16. I win!

They both laugh, knowing that the pictures can be combined to find the total number but the digits cannot be combined in that way.

Next, Kiyo removes her 1 card and places it facedown in her discard pile. She pulls out a 3 card from her pile and then returns it, saying "Three, too small." Then, she pulls out a 2 card from her pile, hesitates, and puts it back, saying "I need something big." Finally, she pulls out a 9, and puts it face up with the 6.

Kiyo: There. It's bigger than your 12. I won.

Carmen: OK. My turn to win next.

Carmen and Kiyo have invented a version of *Double Compare* in which players win alternate rounds. If the player whose turn it is to win has a losing hand, she can choose a replacement card. Although Carmen and Kiyo appear to need more practice counting and combining (they struggled to combine 8 and 5 and arrived at an incorrect total), the teacher decides not to intervene at this point. Although they are not always finding the total of their combinations correctly, they are nonetheless gaining practice counting, comparing, and combining. They are concentrating fully on their work and, as they find winning combinations, they are reasoning about the relative size of numbers and number combinations. The teacher compliments them on developing a collaborative version of the game.

Teacher Note

How Students Approach Five Crayons in All

Five Crayons in All is a complex problem that requires coordinating and keeping track of three pieces of information: the total number of crayons, the number of blues, and the number of reds. In order to solve this How Many of Each? problem, students must count and keep track of a set of objects while comparing the number accumulated so far to the required total. (Do I have 5? Do I need more or fewer?)

At the same time, they need to keep in mind how the two parts combine to reach that total. (I have 7. If I take away 2 things so that I have only 5, now how many blue crayons do I have? How many red crayons?)

Students can solve this problem at levels that are appropriate and challenging for them. There is no single best way of approaching the problem or recording solutions, and you are likely to see many strategies and ways of recording work in your class. As you observe students at work on Five Crayons in All, you can learn a lot about how they are thinking about number combinations, how they solve complex problems, and how they keep track of and record their work. The following examples illustrate a range of approaches observed in one class and demonstrate how the teacher supported students in working at an appropriate level.

Counting to Find Combinations of Five

When the teacher visits Timothy near the start of the session, he has just scattered several blue and red cubes in front of him. He counts out 5 of them and pushes the others aside. Then he counts the 3 blue cubes from his group of 5, touching each cube as he counts it. He counts the 2 red cubes in a similar way. Timothy then sets to work recording his solution. He recounts the blue cubes and draws 3 blue circles on a piece of paper. Looking back at his group of cubes, he draws 2 red circles next to the blue ones. Finally, he counts the circles he has drawn and confirms a total of 5.

When the teacher asks whether he thinks there might be another way to solve the problem, Timothy tells her he has solved the problem. The teacher moves 2 blue cubes together and pushes the other cubes off to the side.

Teacher: What if we just had 2 blue crayons? Then how many reds would we need?

This time, Timothy counts on from the number of blue cubes. He puts down one red and says "3," another and says "4," and another and says "5." Again, he records his solution with blue and red circles.

Timothy begins making another group of blue counters and says he will find how many more reds he needs. When the teacher returns later in the session, Timothy has recorded two more solutions, including one repeated solution. When the teacher asks whether he thinks there are more solutions, he shrugs and says there probably are, and begins to rearrange the cubes on his paper.

Timothy's Work

Many students in the class approached the problem in a manner similar to Timothy. They used counting strategies, such as counting out five objects and then counting the number of each color, or starting with a number of counters of one color and then counting on to find the number of the other color. They were able to keep all the parts of the problem in mind. They had strategies for checking and recording their work. If they found more than one solution, they treated each as a new problem rather than noticing and building on relationships among solutions.

Through repeated experience with this activity and its variations, students become familiar with combinations of numbers such as 5 and 6. Over time, they may begin noticing some relationships among combinations of a number and using these relationships to find new solutions.

Difficulty Coordinating the Parts of the Problem

When the teacher arrives at Ricardo's desk, he has just begun counting a set of blue and red cubes. He counts in a scattered way and arrives at a total of 5 (there are 6). The teacher asks him to count again, more slowly, and reminds him that touching or moving each cube as you count can help you keep track. He counts very slowly and gets six; recounts again, and gets six again.

Teacher: So, you have 6 here. How many do we want?

Ricardo: Six?

Teacher: We need 5 blue and red crayons in all, and we have 6. What could we do to make this 5?

Ricardo: Um . . . take some away?

Teacher: Why don't you try it?

Ricardo pushes aside the two cubes nearest him, apparently without counting the number he is removing. He seems to be thinking only that he has too many cubes and that he needs to remove some. When he says he is finished, the teacher asks him to count the cubes. He does this slowly, gets four, and looks up at the teacher.

Teacher: How many crayons do we want?

Ricardo: Five?

Teacher: Well, we have 4. How could we make it 5?

Ricardo: 4, um, [holds up one finger] 5. [He puts one cube back, so he now has five, and counts them.] 1, 2, 3, 4, 5. I got the answer!

Teacher: Well, you have 5 crayons. Do you remember what we're trying to find?

Ricardo: To get five crayons.

Teacher: OK, yes, we want to get 5, and then we want to know how many are blue and how many are red.

The teacher encourages Ricardo to find a way to record the solution he has found that shows the number of blue crayons and the number of red crayons. She makes a note to ask Ricardo to solve a similar problem about three or four crayons, to see whether he is better able to focus on the target number and on relationships between the total and the two parts with a smaller total.

Working Strategically

When the teacher visits Sarah midway through the session, she has recorded three solutions.

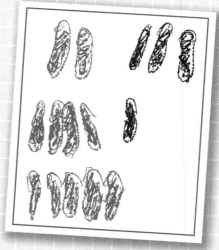

Sarah's Work

Sarah holds up one finger on one hand, and she counts up on her other hand to 5.

Sarah: [talking quietly to herself] 1 and 4. Do I have that yet? No. [She records her new solution.]

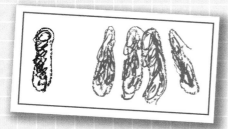

Sarah's Work

Teacher: Can you tell me about how you are finding your solutions?

Sarah: I just did like, 2 red ones and 3 blue ones, and then 4 reds and a blue, and all 5 red, and a red and 4 blues, and I tried to do all the different numbers.

Teacher: All the different numbers? What do you mean?

Sarah: See, I did 1 [points to 1 red and 4 blues], 2 [points to 2 reds and 4 blues], 3 . . . oh, I forgot 3. So 3 and, um, 2. [She records her new solution and glances over her list.] Now I think I have them all. [She points to the corresponding solutions as she lists the number of reds.] 1, 2, 3, 4, 5.

Five Crayons in All gives Sarah a way to solidify and further develop her understanding of combinations of 5. She appears to be finding some combinations (such as 1 and 4) by counting, and to "just know" some others (such as 3 and 2). Unlike many kindergarteners, she does not need to model each solution with crayons or counters. Instead, she works mentally or counts on her fingers. Although she began finding her solutions in a random order, she has developed a strategy for finding all the solutions: she compares new solutions with those already listed to determine whether she has "all the numbers" of red crayons, 1 to 5.

The teacher suggests that Sarah compare her solutions with Mia, who has also found several solutions, but who approached the problem and recorded her work in a different way. Mia found two pairs of "opposite" solutions and recorded them with numbers and words. As Sarah and Mia compare their work, they will have an opportunity to share their different ways of organizing and recording their solutions and to talk about whether they have a complete list and how they know.

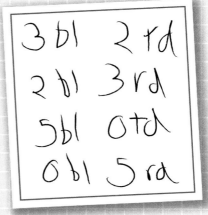

Mia's Work

When the Teacher Records Students' Solutions

When you are recording student work for the class, you will often want to record the work of individuals in different ways. For example, for the activity *Quick Images*, you record each different strategy for remembering the total number of squares in the hidden arrangement in a way that reflects that particular student's thinking.

When students share solutions for Five Crayons in All, however, you need to choose just one way to record because the emphasis is on gathering all of the different solutions. With a single method of recording, students can more easily focus on which solutions are already listed and which new ones could be added.

Students must understand that even though you are recording in a particular way today, they need not always record their solutions in this manner. Emphasize that you are using just one of the many good recording strategies you observed them using in class.

All of you found good ways to record your work—you drew pictures of blue and red crayons, or used blue and red squares, or wrote numbers and words. Today I'm using just one of those ways to record our solutions. Next time I'll use a different way, so we can see all the interesting ways you've found.

Plan to incorporate numbers as you record, regardless of whether the students have used them. To record students' solutions with pictures, your chart might look like this:

On another day, you might record solutions in one of the following ways:

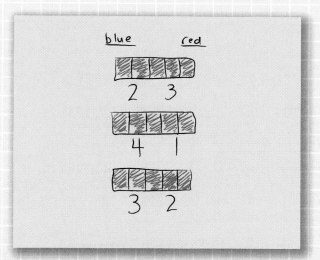

We recommend that you record solutions in the order students give them instead of organizing them into an ordered list. As students work with How Many of Each? type problems, they will begin to see and understand the relationships that exist between the numbers in these problems. Additionally, they will begin to either come up with ways to organize their solutions or be ready to think about ways to organize the information so that they can double-check whether they have found all the possible solutions.

For example, some (but not all) kindergarteners will list solutions from smallest to largest number of blue crayons, while others link "opposite" pairs, such as 3 blue crayons and 2 red crayons with 2 blue crayons and 3 red crayons.

Using a different representation each time exposes students to a variety of approaches and gives them practice interpreting each. You may want to also have a conversation about the different ways students recorded their solutions. This discussion would focus on *how* they showed their solutions, rather than on the solutions themselves. Ask any students who use equations to explain this recording method to the class and to link their equation to one of the pictorial representations. Kindergarteners will vary in their readiness to understand and use equations.

Dialogue Box

Pictures and Numbers

This class has just done *Quick Images* with the following picture.

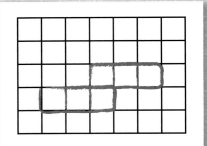

Now, with the picture uncovered, they are discussing the ways they thought about the image to make it easy to remember. Throughout the discussion, notice how the teacher encourages students to think about the number of tiles in each part of the picture.

Teacher: How did you think about this picture so you could remember it when it was covered up?

Sarah: It looks like a snake. It's shaped like a snake.

Teacher: A snake! How did that help you remember the picture?

Shavonne: It goes out at the top, then it goes down, and then it goes the other way [making an S shape with her hand].

Teacher: How many in each part of the snake? Can you come up and show us?

Sarah: Two for the head indicates the two rightmost squares, 2 for the body (the two in the middle), 2 for the tail (the two leftmost squares).

Teacher: Sarah saw 2 in each part—two and two and two. [The teacher copies the shape on the chart paper, circles each group of 2, and labels each circled group with the numeral 2.] Did anyone think about the picture a different way?

Raul: I think it looks like . . . I don't know.

Teacher: That's OK. Keep thinking about it.

Kyle: It's got two of those, um, rows.

Teacher: Two rows? Can you say more about that?

Kyle: A row up there [points to the top], and one there [points to the bottom].

Manuel: I knew both the rows are the same.

Teacher: The same? How?

Manuel: They look the same. They each have 3 squares. [The teacher draws the shape again, circles each row of three, and labels each circled group with a 3.]

Teacher: So we have two ways to think of the picture— 2 and 2 and 2, and 3 and 3. How can we tell how many squares there are in all?

Several students: 6.

Teacher: How do you know there are 6 squares?

Emma: [pointing to the picture with two groups of 3 circled] There's 3 and 3, and 3 and 3 is 6.

Teacher: So there's 3 here, and 3 here, and 3 and 3 is 6. Next to this picture, I'll write 3, that's for this row . . . + 3, that's for this other row . . . equals 6 squares in all. [While speaking, the teacher writes $3 + 3 = 6$.] OK, 3 plus 3 equals 6. Let's look at our picture again. Is there another way you can think of to tell there are 6 in all?

Sarah: I have a way. You can go 2 for the head and 2 for the body is 4. Then there's 2 more.

Teacher: 4 and 2. How could we tell how many that is?

Sarah: 4 and um, [counting on her fingers] 5, 6.

Teacher: So 2 plus 2 equals 4 [writes 2 + 2 = 4 next to the picture with groups of 2 circled]. And then Sarah counted 2 more [writes 5, 6]. So we have 3 and 3 is 6, and we have 2 and 2 is 4 and 2 more is 5, 6. Does anyone have another way to tell how many squares there are?

Jack: You can count them [points to each square as he counts], 1, 2, 3, 4, 5, 6.

Teacher: Counting is always a good way to tell how many. [The teacher draws the arrangement again and writes the numbers 1–6 in the squares.]

These students are developing strategies for analyzing visual images that include relating them to objects (or animals) in the world and thinking about their structure—two rows, with the same number in each. Whatever their strategy, the teacher helps students further develop these skills by pushing them to think about the number of squares in each part or row. As she records, she models ways to see the image in parts as well as the use of numbers, and addition notation when it matches the student's strategy for finding the total.

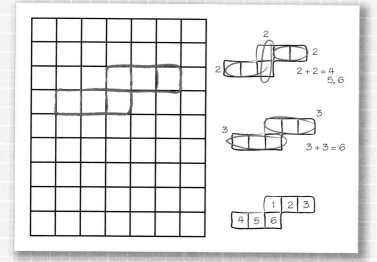

How Are These Stories Different?

Students have acted out and shared solution strategies for each of the following story problems:

Four bees were buzzing around a flower. Three more bees were at the hive. They flew over to join the others at the flower. (Then how many bees were buzzing around the flower?)

Now there were seven bees buzzing around the flower. Two bees left the flower and flew back to the hive. (How many bees were still buzzing around the flower?)

The teacher asks students to think about how the two stories are different.

Teacher: We just solved two problems about bees. In the first one, four bees were at the flower, and three more came and joined them. In the second one, seven bees were at the flower, and two flew away. How are the stories different? Who has an idea?

Jason: Some bees went away, and in the other story, the bees came and joined.

Teacher: Can you tell us what you mean by "joined"?

Jason: It's like when you put things together.

Carmen: It's like a puzzle. You put it together.

Teacher: In the first story, two groups of bees joined together, and in the second, one group of bees went away. Who else has another idea about how the two stories are different?

Kaitlyn: They have different numbers.

Teacher: Different numbers? Can you say more about that?

Raul: There was four and three, and there was seven and two.

Tammy: At first there were seven bees, and then there were only five because two flew away.

Teacher: There were fewer bees at the end of the second story because some bees left to go back to the hive. Were there fewer bees at the end of the first story, when some bees came and joined the group at the flower?

Tammy: No, there were three and then four came, and that's seven.

Note that throughout the discussion, the teacher follows up students' comments about the kinds of actions and the relationships among quantities in the stories. In this way, she begins to draw attention to which actions suggest combining and which suggest separating. The teacher points out that when quantities are combined, the result is more, whereas when they are separated, the result is fewer.

Both of My Numbers Were Bigger

While watching students play *Double Compare,* this teacher was surprised at how many students did not count or add in order to compare the two pairs of cards. She noted two generalizations that seemed to underlie these students' play—that a number plus a big number is more than the same number plus a small number and that two small numbers are less than two big numbers—and decided to pursue those ideas in a class discussion.

Teacher: I noticed something really interesting when I watched you play *Double Compare* today. When I stopped to see Dennis and Jae, this is what their cards looked like.

The teacher lays out 6 and 1, and several students call out "7!" She then deals out a 6 and a 3, and asks the boys to explain how they figured out who had more.

Dennis: I had 6 and he had 6, and then I had a higher number.

Lisa: Me and Mary did that too. 6 and 3 is more than 6 and 1 because the 3 is bigger than 1.

The teacher asks Mary to explain.

Mary: This [pointing to the 3] is big. Even though these are the same [the 6s], this [the 6 and 3] must be more.

Teacher: So it seems like some people noticed something when both players have the same card, like Dennis had a 6 and Jae had a 6.

Jae: When they're the same, you can ignore them.

Dennis: Yeah, they don't matter. You don't have to pay attention to the 6s.

Teacher: When I put down the 6 and 1, I heard a bunch of people say, "that's 7," but when I put down the 6 and 3, no one figured out the total. Would 6 and 3 make a higher number than 6 and 1?

Students call out: 8! 9! 10! They finally settle on 9 by counting all.

Teacher: OK, let's try another one. I saw this when I watched Victor and Latoya. [The teacher lays out two hands, 6 and 5 and 0 and 2.]

Victor: I said "Me" because she got two low numbers.

Latoya: Yeah, because she has two numbers, and 0 isn't even a number. . . . Well it is a number, but it doesn't really count. It's a different kind of number because it's nothing. You don't get anything.

Teacher: I saw Sarah and Mia do something similar [deals 1 and 5 and 0 and 4].

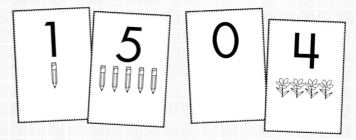

Sarah: This 5 is bigger than this 4, and this 1 is bigger than this 0.

Mia: Both of my numbers were bigger than both of Sarah's. So I said "Me."

Teacher: I was surprised that so many kids were playing this game without counting or adding. It made me wonder, did you ever have a hand that you *had* to count or add? Were there times when you had to count or add to figure it out?

Uncomfortable silence followed, so the teacher put down a 5 and a 1, and a 3 and a 2.

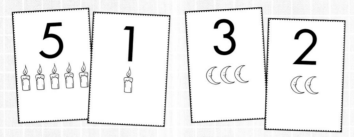

Teacher: Think quietly for a minute. Which hand has more? How do you know?

Mitchell: 5 and 1 is more.

Teacher: How do you know?

Mitchell [pause]: I don't know.

Dennis: 3 + 2 is lower. No, it's higher . . .

Mitchell: I'll count them. [He counts the icons on the cards and announces that 3 and 2 is 5 and 5 and 1 is 6.]

Lisa: That was my idea, too, to count them.

Sarah: Sometimes you can just know, but if you don't, you can count.

After noticing many students using strategies that relied on reasoning about the two pairs, rather than counting or combining, this teacher decided to have a whole class discussion about such methods. A conversation like this calls attention to particular strategies and gives all children an opportunity to think about them and try them out. It also encourages the students who are using the strategies to put them into words. This articulation is an important skill in and of itself and often pushes children's thinking further. It also helps students begin to develop their sense of mathematical argument—an important piece of algebraic work for 5- and 6-year old students.

Student Math Handbook

The *Student Math Handbook Flip Chart* pages related to this unit are pictured on the following pages.

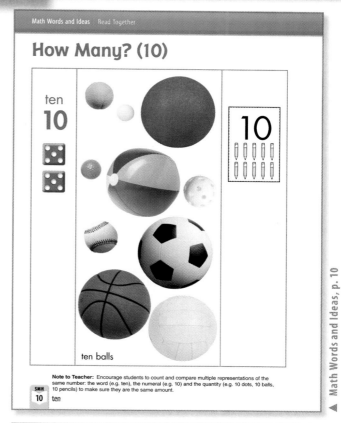

▲ Math Words and Ideas, p. 10

How Many? (10)

ten
10

ten balls

Note to Teacher: Encourage students to count and compare multiple representations of the same number: the word (e.g. ten), the numeral (e.g. 10) and the quantity (e.g. 10 dots, 10 balls, 10 pencils) to make sure they are the same amount.

SMH **10** ten

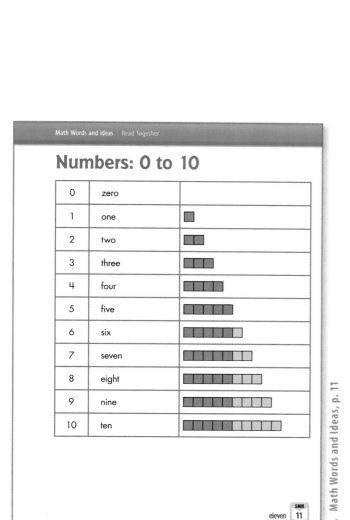

Numbers: 0 to 10

0	zero	
1	one	
2	two	
3	three	
4	four	
5	five	
6	six	
7	seven	
8	eight	
9	nine	
10	ten	

eleven SMH **11**

▲ Math Words and Ideas, p. 11

Numbers: 11 to 19

11	eleven	
12	twelve	
13	thirteen	
14	fourteen	
15	fifteen	
16	sixteen	
17	seventeen	
18	eighteen	
19	nineteen	

SMH **12** twelve

▲ Math Words and Ideas, p. 12

Numbers: 20 to 25

20	twenty	
21	twenty-one	
22	twenty-two	
23	twenty-three	
24	twenty-four	
25	twenty-five	

thirteen **SMH 13**

◄ Math Words and Ideas, p. 13

Ways to Count

When you count, you say one number for each object. You need to keep track of what you are counting.

The last number you say is the total. The total tells you how many are in the group.

Look at how some children count.

Jack puts each button in a cup as he counts it.	*Three . . .*
Abby moves each button as she counts it.	*Four . . .*
Kiyo puts the buttons in a row to count them.	*Eight . . .*

What do you do when you count?

Note to Teacher: *Who Is in School Today?* **Session 2.5.** Use these examples in your first discussion about strategies for counting the objects in the Counting Jar and whenever you discuss how students count.

nineteen **SMH 19**

◄ Math Words and Ideas, p. 19

Counting Jar

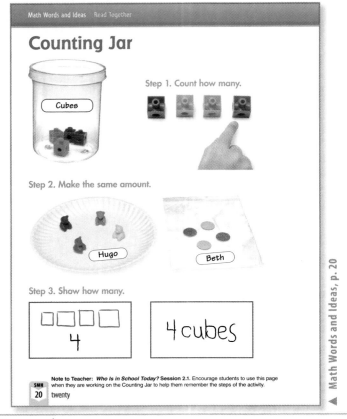

Step 1. Count how many.

Cubes

Step 2. Make the same amount.

Hugo

Beth

Step 3. Show how many.

4

4 cubes

Note to Teacher: *Who Is in School Today?* **Session 2.1.** Encourage students to use this page when they are working on the Counting Jar to help them remember the steps of the activity.

SMH 20 twenty

◄ Math Words and Ideas, p. 20

More

Who has more?

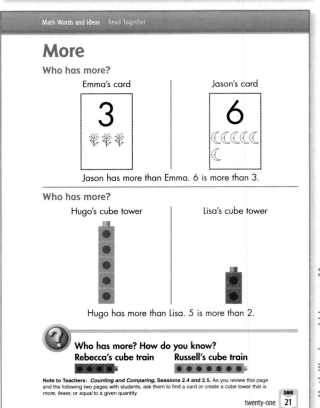

Emma's card	Jason's card
3	6

Jason has more than Emma. 6 is more than 3.

Who has more?

Hugo's cube tower	Lisa's cube tower

Hugo has more than Lisa. 5 is more than 2.

Who has more? How do you know?
Rebecca's cube train   Russell's cube train

Note to Teachers: *Counting and Comparing,* **Sessions 2.4 and 2.5.** As you review this page and the following two pages with students, ask them to find a card or create a cube tower that is *more, fewer,* or *equal* to a given quantity.

twenty-one **SMH 21**

◄ Math Words and Ideas, p. 21

Math Words and Ideas | Read Together

One Fewer

Here are five stars.

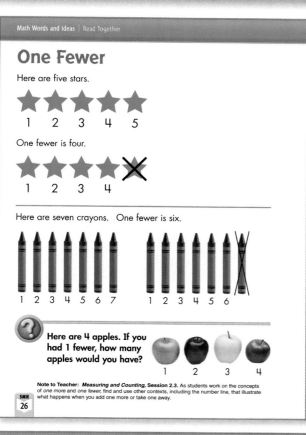

One fewer is four.

1 2 3 4 5

Here are seven crayons.   One fewer is six.

1 2 3 4 5 6 7   1 2 3 4 5 6

Here are 4 apples. If you had 1 fewer, how many apples would you have?

1 2 3 4

Note to Teacher: *Measuring and Counting,* **Session 2.3.** As students work on the concepts of *one more* and *one fewer,* find and use other contexts, including the number line, that illustrate what happens when you add one more or take one away.

SMH
26

▲ Math Words and Ideas, p. 26

Math Words and Ideas | Read Together

Five Tiles

These students are looking at this arrangement of 5 tiles.

Here's how they know that there are 5.

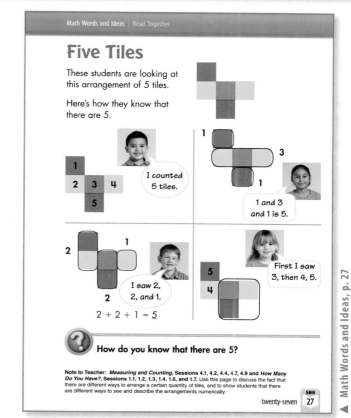

I counted 5 tiles.

1 and 3 and 1 is 5.

I saw 2, 2, and 1.

$2 + 2 + 1 = \underline{5}$

First I saw 3, then 4, 5.

How do you know that there are 5?

Note to Teacher: *Measuring and Counting,* **Sessions 4.1, 4.2, 4.4, 4.7, 4.9** and *How Many Do You Have?,* **Sessions 1.1, 1.2, 1.3, 1.4, 1.6, and 1.7.** Use this page to discuss the fact that there are different ways to arrange a certain quantity of tiles, and to show students that there are different ways to see and describe the arrangements numerically.

twenty-seven

SMH
27

▲ Math Words and Ideas, p. 27

Math Words and Ideas | Read Together

Ways to Make 6

There are different ways to make a number.
Here are some ways to make 6.

Toss the Chips
These students tossed 6 two-color counters.
Some landed on the red side. Some landed on the yellow side.

3 red and 3 yellow   2 red and 4 yellow

Six Tiles
These students arranged 6 tiles.

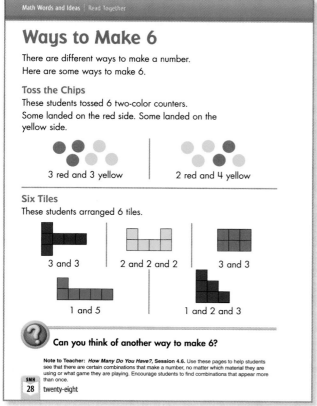

3 and 3   2 and 2 and 2   3 and 3

1 and 5   1 and 2 and 3

Can you think of another way to make 6?

Note to Teacher: *How Many Do You Have?,* **Session 4.6.** Use these pages to help students see that there are certain combinations that make a number, no matter which material they are using or what game they are playing. Encourage students to find combinations that appear more than once.

SMH
28 twenty-eight

▲ Math Words and Ideas, p. 28

Math Words and Ideas | Read Together

More Ways to Make Six

Here are some more ways to make 6.

Total of Six
These students made 6 by using two number cards.

5 1   2 4   6 0

Six Crayons in All
These students made 6 with red and blue crayons.

1 blue and 5 red   2 blue and 4 red

Can you think of another way to make 6?

Note to Teacher: *How Many Do You Have?,* **Session 4.6.** Use these pages to help students see that there are certain combinations that make a number, no matter which material they are using or what game they are playing. Encourage students to find combinations that appear more than once.

twenty-nine

SMH
29

▲ Math Words and Ideas, p. 29

Solving Story Problems

1. Listen to the story.

2. Tell the story in your own words.

3. Solve the problem. You can:

Act it out

Draw pictures

Use cubes

4. Show your solution.

Note to Teacher: *How Many Do You Have?*, **Session 2.5.** Encourage students to use this page in order to remember the steps for solving story problems.

SMH **30** thirty

▲ Math Words and Ideas, p. 30

A Library Story Problem

Here is a story about children at a library.
Three children were reading books at the library.

Then two more children came to the library to read.

What happened in this story?

? **Was this story about putting groups together or about taking away part of a group?**

Note to Teacher: *How Many Do You Have?*, **Sessions 3.3 and 3.5.** After reviewing this page and the following three pages, ask students to visualize, act out, and solve these story problems, as well as the others you create.

thirty-one SMH **31**

▲ Math Words and Ideas, p. 31

Solving a Library Story Problem

Here's the story.
There were 3 children reading books at the library.
Then 2 more children came to the library to read.
How many children in all were reading at the library?
Here are some ways students solved this problem.

These students acted out the story.

1, 2, 3; 4, 5

Mia used cubes.

1 2 3

4 5

I took 3 cubes. Then I took 2 more cubes. Then I counted them.

Jack drew a picture.

I drew the kids. 3 and 2 is 5.

? **How would you solve the problem?**

Note to Teacher: *How Many Do You Have?*, **Sessions 3.3 and 3.5.** After reviewing this page, the previous page, and the following two pages, ask students to visualize, act out, and solve these story problems, as well as others you create.

SMH **32** thirty-two

▲ Math Words and Ideas, p. 32

A Story Problem About Books

Here is a story about books.
Corey was looking for books in the library.
She saw 5 books on the table.

Corey took 2 of the books from the table to read.

What happened in this story?

? **Was this story about putting groups together or about taking away part of a group?**

Note to Teacher: *How Many Do You Have?*, **Sessions 3.3 and 3.5.** After reviewing this page, the previous two pages, and the following page, ask students to visualize, act out, and solve these story problems, as well as others you create.

thirty-three SMH **33**

▲ Math Words and Ideas, p. 33

Solving a Story Problem About Books

Corey was looking for books in the library.
She saw 5 books on the table.
Corey took 2 of the books from the table to read.
How many books were left on the table?

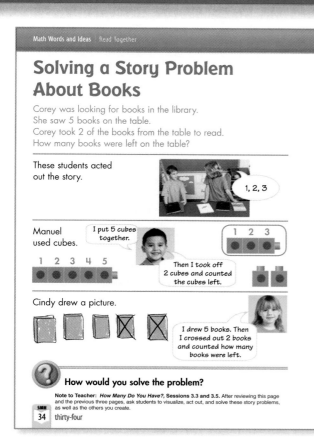

These students acted out the story.

1, 2, 3

Manuel used cubes.

I put 5 cubes together.

1 2 3

1 2 3 4 5

Then I took off 2 cubes and counted the cubes left.

Cindy drew a picture.

I drew 5 books. Then I crossed out 2 books and counted how many books were left.

How would you solve the problem?

Note to Teacher: *How Many Do You Have?*, **Sessions 3.3 and 3.5.** After reviewing this page and the previous three pages, ask students to visualize, act out, and solve these story problems, as well as the others you create.

SMH
34 thirty-four

◀ Math Words and Ideas, p. 34

Measuring with Cubes

These students used cubes to measure the length of some objects in their classroom.

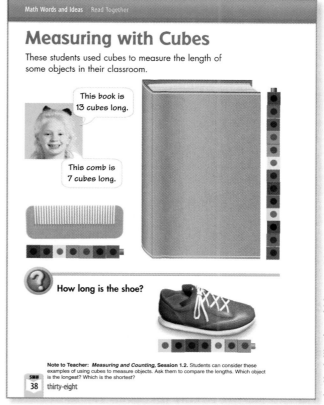

This book is 13 cubes long.

This comb is 7 cubes long.

How long is the shoe?

Note to Teacher: *Measuring and Counting*, **Session 1.2.** Students can consider these examples of using cubes to measure objects. Ask them to compare the lengths. Which object is the longest? Which is the shortest?

SMH
38 thirty-eight

◀ Math Words and Ideas, p. 38

Index

IN THIS UNIT

W

Whole-number operations. *See also*
 Addition; Subtraction. 13–14
Words
 representing combining/separating
  with, 14, 75–77, 93–94
 representing sets with, 94
Writing opportunities, 16

Z

Zero, 18–19, 145